Cottage Industries

Cottage Industries

by

Valerie Porter

SWAN·HILL
PRESS

Copyright © 1992 by Valerie Porter

First published in the UK in 1992 by Swan Hill Press
an imprint of Airlife Publishing Ltd.

British Library Cataloguing in Publication Data

A catalogue record for this book
is available from the British Library.

ISBN 1 85310 165 6

Printed by Livesey Ltd., Shrewsbury

Swan Hill Press

An imprint of Airlife Publishing Ltd
101 Longden Road, Shrewsbury SY3 9EB, England

Contents

Introduction

The crafts of the countryside were once essential to rural life: they were downright practical. Too often now, they are relegated to working rural museums and nostalgic books, or are practised as hobbies which might bring a sense of creative satisfaction to the practitioner but belittle the craft by meeting no practical need. Today, crafted goods are more often sold purely for their decorative value and find a place in urban environments where they are never really quite at home. They bring pleasure to those who yearn for a countryside they have probably never lived with, that exists mainly in imagination and from which, should they find themselves transplanted, they would no doubt flee within a couple of years.

There is no harm in bringing pleasure but there is even greater pleasure in an article which is also useful. For as long as there have been real villages, there has also been rural poverty and cottage dwellers have supplemented their livelihood by converting garden, smallholding and wild produce into items which could be used in the home or exchanged for other goods. Later, as land and work grew scarce and times even harder, they began to depend more heavily on their cottage industries and became better organised, more intent on exchanging than using their own goods. In due course, cottagers were fashioning raw materials other than those they had grown or reared themselves and they sold their wares at markets and fairs, or through the agents who began to dominate the cottage industries, bringing raw materials to the cottagers as they collected the finished goods. Later still, the cottagers moved into towns and cities to exchange their labour and skills for wages which were often pitiable. They were finally losing touch with the land which had originally been the source of their raw materials, and with that they lost more than a degree of practical independence and ingenuity.

Today, whether in farmhouses, villages or towns, cottagers can find pleasure and perhaps a little profit in their home crafts, some of which really do become 'industries' rather than hobbies. A few still manage to produce their own raw materials from the land and to handle it through all the stages of growing and rearing, harvesting, and conversion into a finished article for their own use or for sale. This book is largely intended for such lucky individuals in that its main aim is to suggest how smallholders and gardeners can add value to their produce by creating an end product from it.

Although the book seeks to re-establish that vital and traditional link between production of the raw material and its conversion to useful or decorative items, creativity need not be restricted by a lack of space in which to grow plants or raise livestock. There is material aplenty all around you and there are also many sources from which you can buy basic materials for cottage crafts. Buying in might be more convenient, though inevitably less satisfying than being able to boast that you have knitted a sweater to your own design from the wool of your own sheep, known to you from lambhood and carefully bred for good, natural fleece colours for your spinning wheel, or that your very own windowbox grew the herbs and perfumes in your home-made cosmetics, or that the fruitbowl on the table (and the table itself) was made by you from the wood of your own trees and contains the produce of your orchard and hedgerows.

★   ★   ★

Cottage crafts tend to develop from hobbies and to remain supplementary to other sources of income, or even a drain on them, but they should not be belittled for such unassuming beginnings. They have the potential to become cottage industries, to grow into truly successful enterprises, if that is what you wish — and sometimes almost of their own accord, whatever your original intentions. A hobby that begins in a small way in the kitchen or living room can develop a life of its own and demands space of its own, too. Be warned!

Success is more likely if you make use of an interest and skill you already have but which you need to perfect before you can even consider selling the results to other people. There comes a moment — perhaps imperceptibly, perhaps quite suddenly — when your hobby becomes a trade and that is when your standards must become relentlessly and *consistently* high. It is at this point that many ventures collapse. Even if you do succeed in finding or creating a demand for your product, you must be able to sustain production quality and quantity so that the demand continues to be met, or your customers will lose faith and interest. The outpourings from a house cow might seem quite overwhelming at times, when you don't really want all that milk, but she will be dry for several weeks at a time — and then what happens to all those locals who have come to love your blackberry yoghurt? They will find another source and might not come back to you when Jemima calves again. Hence this book includes encouragement about marketing, which in the context of an industry, even on a cottage scale, is as important as creative skills.

The emphasis, however, is on creativity. Some of the crafts described in the following chapters are simple enough to learn and require imagination more than skill if you want to exploit them in the marketplace; others need personal tuition or apprenticeship, and some demand literally years of experience. For some, it will be easy to find a teacher; for others, the masters have already largely faded away and you will have to learn the hard way, by book and experiment.

This book will give basic guidance on many cottage and rural crafts, with information about where to find out more. Above all it is intended to inspire creative *ideas* — the true raw material of any venture. Anybody can make a basket, and many can make it well, but it takes a creative imagination to produce a basket with a difference, a basket with your personal imprint of originality, perhaps because of using unexpected materials or making unusual shapes or dreaming up ingenious applications for basket-making techniques. Capture tradition but do not be enthralled to it: use the traditional skills but with flair and originality, and enhance them with techniques and materials your great grandparents were born too soon to know. Weave the skills of the past into the materials and techniques of the present. The cottagers of the past had considerable skills and it is up to you to keep those skills alive and give present generations the chance to appreciate the individuality of craft in an age of mass production. The cottagers of the past are standing at your shoulder, watching with interest to see how you honour them. Let them guide your hand.

1 Wood

Wood is available in most parts of Britain, be it from hedgerows, coppices or trees grown for timber. It is an infinitely adaptable and renewable resource and the growth of trees can be simply taken for granted or deliberately managed. Trees offer a wondrous combination of practicality and beauty — and so does wood: it is the raw material for a huge range of traditional crafts, many of them ideal cottage industries.

Coppice

A coppice is an area in which certain hardwood species are harvested in a regular cycle by cutting them close to the ground and allowing the 'stools' to sprout again, producing multiple stems which are grown on for harvesting in the next cycle. The same rootstock can be harvested for several cycles and can be productive at intervals for

From left to right: homemade froe (for splitting out chestnut palings), small adze, old grasshook blade used as a drawknife, and side-axe. All resting on upturned workhorse, with woodman's barrow in the background.

Close-up of adze showing the curve of the blade.

more than a century if properly managed. In fact it is quite possible to rejuvenate neglected coppice and make rootstocks considerably more than a century old productive again.

Coppice is thus a self-perpetuating system of production and a very efficient use of wooded land, with a much quicker turnover than high forest (i.e. trees grown to full size for harvesting mainly as sawn timber — coppice stems are usually less than 8in in diameter when cut) and in the past the coppices were vital to rural life: they were the source of fuel and of nearly every type of useful everyday wooden article. However, the system is now almost dying on its feet for want of skilled labour by craftsmen who rely on handmade tools, muscle power and a good eye rather than machinery. The young tend to reject the hard work and solitude of the coppice and the old have no one to whom they can pass on their craft.

Hazel coppices were once the source of a wide range of useful rural cottage items made from flexible, small-diameter rods harvested at relatively short intervals. The acreage of managed hazel coppice has been reduced to less than a twentieth of its area a generation ago but there is still plenty of hazel waiting to be worked again and turned into beanpoles, peaboughs, firewood, stakes for laid hedges, crate rods, wattle panels, thatching spars, riverbank revetts, ship fenders, sheep hurdles, barrel hoops, fish traps, pleached fencing, baskets, walking sticks — and that is all from a single species. A well managed mixed coppice including combinations of, say, sweet chestnut, ash, birch, alder, lime, willow, oak and sycamore as well as hazel could produce materials for all kinds of fencing, charcoal, tools, turnery and other woodcrafts which use rotationally harvested timber and brushwood. If planted with standards (trees left to grow to greater maturity), such coppices could also supply nuts, carving woods, bark, sap and resin, extending the already wide range of possibilities. Work the coppice in rotation so that a different patch is harvested each year or so for continuous production; cut your poles from November to March, peel them while they are still green if you want to remove the bark, and then spend a pleasant summer working them up as you wish.

Coppicework is one of the most satisfying enterprises for smallholders who have enough land to grow a patch of suitable trees and who are interested in self-sufficiency and rural crafts. If you are lucky enough (as I am) to live in an area where old cleavers are still at work in their coppices, make all haste to watch, listen and learn before they fade into the past.

The necessary skills range from a most basic wielding of a chainsaw for producing firewood or fencing materials, to the woodland and yard arts of splitting pales or making wattle panels, gates, sheep hurdles and walking sticks, and the highly skilled workshop crafts such as turnery.

Firewood

As a cottage industry (though hardly meriting the title of a craft), the sale of firewood is one of the simplest as long as you have a chainsaw (and have been properly trained in its use), an axe, a pick-up vehicle and an area in which the logs can be seasoned for a year. A more interesting venture might be a small energy centre selling wood-burning stoves as well as wood and, for the more ambitious, your own charcoal for barbecues and perhaps bagged straw briquettes for stoves and open fires. You could extend the idea to embrace other forms of energy (visit the Centre for Alternative Technology in Wales) and perhaps give serious thought to the potential for recycling unlikely waste materials into useful power sources. Sometimes the individual on the ground or in the field can be more creative than whole teams of scientists in the lab.

Charcoal

Charcoal burning is the art of reducing wood to a concentrated, lightweight fuel by smouldering it in controlled conditions without admitting air (which would cause the whole lot to catch fire and you end up with ashes instead of charcoal). It is a coppice craft of considerable skill, once practised by itinerants who would set up camp in the coppice, building themselves a temporary home out of the materials to hand. Now most charcoal production is on a large scale in substantial, automated, permanent kilns but there are still a few independent charcoal burners, though they are more likely to use semi-portable steel drum kilns than to build an old-style clamp of wood and earth. In some less developed countries, however, charcoal burning is practised on a very local scale in village kilns or even in old oildrums for small quantities.

Charcoal is carbonised wood and its energy content is twice as high as that of the same weight of firewood, while it can fetch a price several times higher. It is easy to handle and store; it burns at a higher temperature than wood and does so without smoke. The principle steps in charcoal production are:

1 Drive the moisture out of the wood by heating it, using some of the crop for the initial combustion.
2 At temperatures above 270°C, volatile gases and liquids will be released. The gases burn readily in the presence of limited air and produce enough heat to continue the process.
3 When most of the gases have been burnt off, the smoke escaping from the kiln becomes thin and turns from grey to blue or becomes transparent. Carbonisation is complete and the system must be immediately shut down and allowed to cool. If air is admitted at this stage, the charcoal will be reduced to ashes.

Unless you are prepared to learn the art of clamp-building for its own sake, you need a steel drum kiln. It is quite a simple piece of equipment: there are two large rings, one on top of the other, with a conical lid over all, and perhaps four separate inlets, each with its own fire and chimney. Lay some 'stringers' at the base of the bottom ring — lengths of wood fanning out like the spokes of a wheel — and then throw in plenty of faggots (bundles of brushwood and trimmings) to fill the ring. Put the second ring in place and fill to the top with coppiced logs. Top it with the lid, light your fires (which will take time) and burn for perhaps 16–24 hours until you see the smoke changing. Close down the kiln, sealing it to stop the fires. When it is completely cool, remove the top ring: the bottom one should be full of beautiful charcoal. Shovel it out, putting it through grids to sieve off the larger pieces, which should be returned to the kiln, while the rest can be bagged and sold. If you build a clamp instead, the whole job takes considerably longer: stacking is a matter of great care to a pattern rather than throwing the logs in at random, and then you will have to sit and watch it for anything up to ten days or so while it carbonises, making quite sure that any cracks in the earth-and-sod jacket are filled before the fire breaks out.

Fencing

Workaday fencing posts are a major product of sweet chestnut coppicing: the species, like oak, has naturally durable heartwood and does not need to be treated with preservatives. Of the softwoods (which cannot be coppiced as they will not sprout again from the stump), larch and western red cedar are also durable in their heart-wood. Other species need to be treated to protect them from rotting under the onslaught of fungi and insects.

Most fungi only attack wood if its moisture content is more than about 20 per cent. Seasoning will therefore reduce the risk but the seasoned wood must be kept dry for the rest of its life to retain its immunity. If it is in direct contact with the ground — for example as a post — or cannot be protected from wet weather, it needs treatment. In the case of direct ground contact, merely brushing or spraying with preservative is useless: the wood must be thoroughly impregnated. Creosote is the traditional wood preservative in these circumstances and needs to be applied with the aid of heat, thus:

1 Season the wood first, until it has lost at least 25 per cent of its fresh-felled weight.

2 Put a metal tank on a few bricks so that you can make a fire underneath.

3 Put the posts into the tank and fill up with cold creosote.

4 Heat the whole lot up to 180°F (80°C) and maintain at that temperature for a couple of hours.

5 Allow it to cool. It is during the *cooling* that absorption takes place: leave the posts in the creosote until it is cold.

Rustic work

Apart from fencing, simple coppice poles are used for all kinds of 'rustic' work, the essence of which is lack of uniformity. The rustic craftsman exploits the natural branching and curving of the stem, or uses poles just as they are, complete with bark, in preference to the precision of sawn timber. Rustic structures must be reassuringly solid and durable, and they are deceptively simple.

Pointed fencing poles sorted and stacked, ready for collection.

There is plenty of skill in some rustic work and an artistic eye is important.

The simplest applications for rustic poles are in the creation of *adventure trails* — structures to jump over, scramble over, teeter along, crawl under, swing from and so on. Good adventure trails, however, are far from haphazard: they are carefully designed to take into account different ages and abilities, offering challenges to children, teenagers, parents, panting office workers and superfit soldiers. Every village should have an adventure trail!

Every village should certainly have a *children's playground* and here rustic work can come into its own — really solid climbing frames, supports for slides, play-houses, forts and anything else that a good rustic craftsman can dream up. Safety must be a top priority, of course, and great care needs to be taken to ensure that there is no

risk from nails, loose joints, sharp edges, slippery surfaces or splinters.

My own village boasts such a playground, created by just such a craftsman whose yard is set in the heart of the village. He is a man who abhors conformity and straight lines and is a genius at seeing the potential of living trees and dead branches as he wanders through the woods. Confronted with a large old stump, he will pause for a quiet word with his Good Lord who, invariably it seems, suggests a use for what to many eyes might be an unpromising lump of dereliction and then advises him how to deal with it. The yard is a glorious riot of imaginative tree-houses and wendy houses (his speciality), bird tables, nest boxes, rabbit hutches, dog kennels, climbing frames, forts — even half a galleon complete with masts, cabins, decks, wooden cannons and a gang plank, waiting to be transported

RUSTIC DESIGNS

Wonky wendyhouses (deliberately so).

Children's bird-tables and craftsman's stool.

to an urban playground on the coast. The place is a source of considerable inspiration to the village children who are invited to spend a summer week creating their own masterpieces from unlikely bits and pieces of branches and offcuts. The craftsman's work is deceptively rustic, however, and the children soon realise that his designs are really quite complex and require a great deal of artistic skill and sheer woodcraft. But they all go home happy, clutching a wonky birdhouse or a wobbly garden chair, made under his kind and watchful eye.

The story of this rustic workshop has a salutory twist. The craftsman in this case is indeed a man of great kindness and of endless creative vision and skill but, as he is the first to admit, he is not a businessman: time. schedules, deadlines, estimates, accounts, bills and other figurings are alien to him and, sadly, he has recently been bought out by an apparently benevolent saviour who has in fact turned this gentle genius out of his own yard so that it can be 'developed'. The village is losing one of its best known and best loved landmarks and commerce is once again riding roughshod over craftsmanship.

Apart from catapults and bows (and perhaps you will be inspired to make more sophisticated projectiles like boomerangs), the simplest rustic product which our village children annually enjoy creating, and putting to good use in the garden, is a *bird table*, perhaps no more than a piece of hardboard or plank supported by a rough pole but usually a great deal more elaborate once a child's imagination takes control — a roof to keep the birdfood dry, perhaps of bark-covered slabwood (the outer offcuts left when squaring a trunk for sawmill planks) or thatch, and assorted perches — or a more ambitious *birdhouse*, of quite a size, shaped like a poultry ark with a roof of tightly packed lengths of roundwood, supported on a strong, naturally branched pole which also serves as a post for climbing roses and clematis, while vines scramble up wires attached to each corner of the birdhouse floor.

Typical rustic work includes garden *pergolas* and screens, from simple archways to complex patterns made with various lengths and thicknesses of roundwood forming diagonals, triangles and squares — partly to support the structure but mainly decorative. A 19th-century American book described several rustic structures in New York's Central Park — a rustic *bridge* supported by forked trunks with crisscross poles forming side railings, a shady covered *arbour* over a pathway where the forked trunks supported a latticed pole roof smothered with climbing plants, a large ornate *summerhouse* of four forked uprights supporting an elaborate roof in which full use was made of the decorative potential of curved and curling pieces of roundwood, with wooden shingles to keep out the rain and sliced tree trunks set as steps up to a rustic bench. For a simpler rural summer-house, use a few poles as uprights, dug into the ground, with other poles fastened across them (nails for the impatient, or withies for the true rustic), then weave twigs in wattle fashion among the poles to form the top and sides and plant scented climbers and trailers to ramble over the structure, or give it a thatched roof. There is a fine dividing line between pleasant rustic and twee . . .

I would not dream of telling a child how to make a *treehouse* — the joy of them is the sense of personal achievement — but you can make them truly elaborate. Indeed, some notable eccentrics have produced magnificent treehouses, several storeys high or in series connected by precarious treetop walkways, and some have been made deliberately by more down-to-earth builders with an eye to accommodation for tourists.

On a lesser scale, simple *nesting boxes* can be fashioned from sections of hollow branch or trunk, given a weatherproof top and — the important factor — an access hole of the right size for the expected bird. My village craftsman once made me a typically asymmetrical mailbox, designed to take milk deliveries on one side in an open alcove and with an ingeniously enclosed 'post box' on the other with a wavy-outlined posting slot to receive the letters and a top-hinged door so that they could be removed. Wavy lines were the essence of the whole edifice (I had actually asked for a straightforward, straight-edged box but it was not in his nature to create such things). The first year, nesting great tits occupied the postbox by taking advantage of the wavy slit. The next year, though the slit was deliberately blocked, they discovered the almost ideal

entry hole made by the wavy edge of the box's wall where it met the hinged flap (by then a little warped at the hinges so that it did not close fully) and they set about enlarging the hole to their needs, although the wood was inch-thick oak. It took them a while, but they had an in-hole at one side of the flap and an out-hole at the other, and never did they or their young leave by the in-hole or enter by the exit!

If you are more serious about building for wild birds, look at the Bibliography for some very good books which give technical details of the needs of different species and good working drawings.

The rustic *windowbox* is a typical example of the imaginative use of simple materials. Take a plain pine box as a foundation and cover it with a pattern of small poles, split in half but with bark intact. At its simplest, the splits can be set close together, vertically, but it is much more fun to create patterns — diamonds, slants, horizontals mingled with verticals, adding the contrast of perhaps silver birch against a dark-barked wood, or other prettily barked species.

Rustic *furniture* is simple enough to devise — benches, chairs and tables can be made from roundwood or by using thick, untrimmed planks retaining their natural edges. Opportunists with the skill and equipment to do so are quick to exploit the unexpected crop of trees felled by severe gales and some have learned the art of carving one-piece benches out of a solid tree trunk, using a chainsaw to break the back

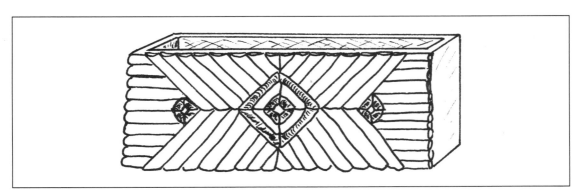

Rustic windowbox decorated with roundwood and halfround sections.

of the labour involved. In 1990, at a historic meeting in a country hideaway (with the world's press in attendance), President Gorbachev and Chancellor Kohl were filmed perched on simple rustic chairs made from sections of tree-trunk cut across halfway up to form the seat, around a huge trunk with knee-holes hewn out of it to form a table.

Woodland crafts

Here are some of the basic methods for traditional crafts using woodland produce. Many of them sound deceptively simple and you will only discover the degree of real skill needed when you actually try your own hand at them. Measurements are deliberately given in imperial units — the crafts had been carried on for centuries before metrication was introduced to Britain.

Chestnut paling

Split chestnut poles into pales. To make them up into lengths of paling, drive two substantial posts into the ground ten yards apart (a traditional length — if you visit the old family firm of Astolat near Guildford you will see that all their sheds are tailored to this size) and stretch two or three pairs of wire between them, passing them through holes drilled through the posts and attaching them to tension arms. At one end, twist each pair of wires together for a few turns with the help of a windlass, then insert the first pale between each pair. Now twist the windlass in the *opposite* direction to secure the pale. Insert the next pale and continue in this way, twisting alternate ways after each pale. You can do the work by hand or invest in fairly expensive machinery. In the latter case, think of other applications for

SHEEP HURDLES

Shaping with a drawknife, using a treadle-operated brace.

the equipment. What else could be wired together in this way, or needs twisting? Work on it!

Hazel wattle panels

Use a heavy piece of timber 7ft long as a 'mould': it should be slightly curved in a horizontal plane and should have ten holes drilled into it to support the uprights of the panel as you work. Cut your uprights to length and set them in the holes: the two outer ones (shores) are round, with pointed tips so that they can be driven into the ground when the panel is in use, while the eight inner ones (sails) can be round or cleft. Starting near the middle at the base, weave in some green uncleft rods (spurs) to give a firm rim. When you reach the end of the row, give the rod a deft half-twist round the shore so that you don't break the fibres, and continue weaving in this way for a few inches before changing to cleft rods. (Use a

billhook or adze to cleave them.) As if you were making a basket or working at a loom, keep pressing the rods down to close any gaps: use the back of the billhook or your foot or knee. Overlap new rods as they are introduced into the weaving and make sure that the half-twist at each end results in each face being uniform — all white wood on one side of the panel and all bark on the other. If the panel is for sheep, make a traditional twilley hole so that a shepherd can carry the panels on a pole. Finish off with round poles again for the last few inches, trim off to make a tidy job and then stack the panels convex side upwards to allow them to flatten and thus tighten themselves.

Sheep hurdles

These strong, lightweight gates are usually made of ash, chestnut, willow or oak. They are usually about 6ft long and waist-high. For each hurdle you need two end uprights

The hurdle completed.

(heads or spiles), a shorter central upright (right-up), some rails or ledges (six for sheep) and two diagonal braces or stretchers. All the pieces are of cleft poles, riven when green. The uprights should be tapered with a billhook to blunted points so that they can be driven into the ground, but leave the tops flat. The rails and braces are more or less six-sided. The unit relies on reasonably good mortise joints between the heads and the rails (simply drill two holes for each and knock out the wood between them with a chisel), but the braces and central upright are secured to the rails with nails. Set all the rails into their mortise holes in one of the heads, then tap the other head into position and square up the structure before nailing on the braces and central bar.

Many sheepfarmers now use tubular-metal hurdles instead of wooden ones. They are more convenient to buy, no doubt, but not necessarily either lighter, stronger or more durable, and the making of a metal product is bound to use more irreplaceable energy and raw materials.

Cribs and cradles

Haycribs for field use are simple to make from pliable hazel or willow rods. While they are still green, form them into curved half-hoop ribs with their ends pushed into holes drilled through a pair of long poles strutted with crossbars to maintain the crib's shape. Nail a few more poles along the sides for greater rigidity and to keep the hay in place. It could also serve as a plant holder or the basis of a cage for catching up pheasants and chickens.

If you are more ambitious, try hewing a wooden manger. I have seen some beautiful old wooden mangers, standing forgotten in derelict cowhouses and licked to a high polish by generations of cattle determined to secure every last morsel of food.

PEG-MAKING

Nailing on a tin-strip before splitting the peg.

Beginning the split.

Spars and pegs

Thatching spars (or spurs, sprays, specks, spicks, spitts, stables, buckles, broaches, brotches) are used to pin new thatch to old or to secure the liggers (hazel or willow rods, also known as runners or sways, which run horizontally over the thatch to hold it in place). Spars are simply lengths of hazel or willow, about 2ft long (60cm), split with a billhook so that they are more or less triangular in cross-section. The thatcher will bend them into a hairpin shape, with a twist at the angle to avoid breaking the fibres.

Clothespegs are made from short pieces of round willow, bound first with a strip of tin (held by a tiny nail) and then split to the point of the binding. The ends of the peg are smoothed and tapered.

Besoms

There are several broomsquires in Surrey whose besoms are so much in demand for local golf-courses and racehorse stables that

they make their wares all year round and employ young apprentices to help them meet the endless orders. Besoms are also popular as general yard brooms and for sweeping up leaves, invigorating tired lawns and other garden tasks, but they were once much more widely used — by butchers and fishmongers to whisk away flies, by carpet makers to brush off the fluff, by ironworkers to flick away hot flakes, and perhaps above all in brewing and vinegar-making.

Think of the Old Bull and Bush, for example. The 'bush' was originally a besom hung outside an alehouse as a symbol of brewing: besoms stirred fermenting liquors and were hung up to dry before the next brewing session — they became well impregnated with yeast and thus helped the new fermentation to start working quickly. They were used by every brewery to aerate the frothy barm (hence 'barmy' as a term for silliness — frothiness) and by every pub to whisk up their own barm in

THE BROOMSQUIRE

Using the broom-horse to wire the birch twigs. The pedal controls the run of the wire.

Cleaning the handle with a straight-bladed drawknife.

Refining the shape of the handle with a curved drawknife.

Banging the handle into the broom.

wooden pails just before the village women came along to buy a jamjar's worth for home baking. Swales — shorter, square-cut bundles of birch brush without any handles — were designed to aerate and filter vinegar: they helped to create acetic acid in malt liquor vats and collected the sludge.

Use birch twigs (cut from October to May, ideally when the catkins are still on them) or heather (cut in full bloom towards the end of August) or, for a softer broom, ling. Trim the branchlets to length and bundle them in armfuls, cross-stacking them to season over the summer, then work them up in winter. The methods of birch and heather brooms are similar. First make up a core, either a handful of small twigs or sprigs ('snuffings') or a doubled-over bundle from the stack as a dolly. Surround the core with brushwood and bind it tightly with a couple of wires or split, soaked and peeled willow withies. You will need a broom horse to compress the bundle adequately, or at least a modified woodman's cradle and grip. Chop off the butts for a square finish at the top and then force in a pointed handle (birch or hazel pole) exactly through the centre of the bundle. Up-end it so that you can bang the top of the handle down against a hard surface, which will drive the other end well into the broom. Drill a hole through the bottom of your broomstick so that a wooden peg or nail can be driven in to secure it. Bundle the besoms in dozens — traditionally thirteen to the dozen — then pile them into your cart and trot around selling them to stables, country houses and garden centres.

The original broom-making plant was of the *Cytisus* family of brooms. There is also an evergreen woodland shrub known as butcher's broom which has stiff shoots with stiff, spiny leaves, and it was, literally, used by butchers to sweep off their blocks. In America special 'broom corn' millet was grown to make straw brooms (you need a thick, strong type of straw): it was harvested before the frosts by cutting off the heads with about a foot of stalk attached and drying them on the barn floor. The seeds were then combed off and the stem cut off about 6in from the 'brush' and stood in water up to the brush for an hour or two to soften before being carefully placed in order in a bunch to form the broom.

Rakes

It takes a greater variety of skills to make wooden hayrakes than besoms. They are beautiful implements, with heads from perhaps 30in to 4ft across but very light to use. They have three components: a long, smooth handle (usually of seasoned ash), a head of cleft or sawn ash or willow, and a set of tines.

The handle, or stail, is not simply a rough pole cut from the coppice: it must be steamed for straightening in a setting brake, shaved smooth with a drawknife so that it is nicely rounded, tapered by means of a stail engine (a rotary plane something like a pencil sharpener in effect) and then bound with metal or leather strips about 20in from the head end so that it can be carefully split (like a wooden clothespeg) and fanned out to support the head.

The head itself is split off from a triangular cleft, shaped with a side-axe and smoothed with a drawknife, then bored through with holes every two or three inches to take the tines. You also need holes to take the stail ends, which are driven through so that they project a little and are secured with screws or nails.

The tines are first of all roughly cleft from a billet of wood and then rounded by being forced through a tine former — a 6in length of half-inch iron pipe with a sharp cutting edge at one end. Drive the finished tines through their head holes and sharpen their tips at an appropriate angle for raking. If any come loose later, use the old cart-driver's trick of soaking the wood in water to swell and tighten everything back into place.

Snaiths

A stail is a long, straight tool handle which can often be fashioned quite simply from a straight-growing, freshly cut pole, trimmed to shape if necessary with a drawknife, whereas a snaith or snead is the beautifully shaped and balanced handle of a scythe. It forms a gentle double curve that almost flows with the rhythmic swing of an expert scyther and the tool is as much a work of art as its user is an artiste. It is perfectly designed for economy of effort and efficiency of cut, and is also a very personal implement: every snaith should be made to suit the individual who will use it and balanced to the user's physique and style of action. Such scythes still have their uses, especially for dealing with orchard grass or for haymaking awkward patches where machinery is unsuitable. I used to mow an acre of meadow hay with a scythe, albeit inexpertly, and then used an old wooden hayrake whose stail had been polished smooth by use in an earlier generation: both implements were delightfully light and pleasant to handle, and with the strength to outlive any machine-made tool.

Snaiths are typically of coppiced ash, peeled and rounded with a drawknife. The curves are achieved by steaming the handle and then shaping it around and between pegs, leaving it to set. The wooden pegs are driven into heavy pieces of timber on the ground, or upright posts. The same technique can be used for shaping poles for other requirements (practical or artistic) if you do not feel like simply clamping greenwood and leaving it for a year or so to set its shape, rather than steaming it first.

Walking sticks

Almost any coppice species can be harvested for walking sticks. In the past coppices and country hedgerows were important sources of materials for simple forked thumbsticks, knobheaded and cross-headed sticks and curved canes. Saplings and coppice poles can be specially trained to grow into interesting shapes, or you can look out for natural distortions — perhaps the convolutions caused by honeysuckle (woodbine) coiling itself around a stem. The so-called tree cabbage or cow cabbage grows

a stem long enough and woody enough to make a good stick, too, and indeed the stalks are so tough that they were used as rafters under thatch on old farm buildings: they could last fifty years if kept dry. The cabbage leaves were fed fresh to cattle or were mixed with sour milk and bran for ducks, geese and pigs.

A green stick can often be straightened by simply hanging it vertically from a beam with a weight at its end and leaving it to season. To make a simple curved handle for a hook stick, use a straight rod and steam it in a moist sandbath, heated from below, until the wood is pliable enough to be gently and carefully persuaded into shape around a former without splitting. Tape or bind it into a tighter curve than you need and leave it to set its shape (the curve is bound to spring open a little when it is released). Season the stick for a few months in a dry, airy place, then smooth it down and polish or

Collection of iron crooks and carved heads.

varnish it, adding a metal or rubber ferrule to its tip.

More elaborate sticks have carved handles, or heads of different materials altogether such as bone, antler, horn, resin or metal (as in a shepherd's crook). The main problem is to shank the handle firmly and smoothly to the stick, especially if it is a practical crook designed to restrain a sheep who would rather be elsewhere. Crook-making is a special art involving forgework and there used to be some famous crooksmiths in sheep country such as the South Downs, where the Sussex village of Pyecombe became synonymous with a particularly successful long-shanked design of crook. Today, however, most shepherds use light-weight metal crooks, though some of the iron ones are still made for shepherds of a different kind — those in the Church.

Clogs

Oh well, if you must! There are two main stages in traditional clog-making. The clogger works in the coppice, roughly cutting clog soles from alder or sycamore: use green wood up to 18in in diameter, cut into butts about a foot long, and cleave the butts into blocks with an axe or with beetle and wedge; trim the blocks roughly to shape with a side-axe, then chop away with a stock-knife to pare the block into a rounded approximate clog shape and to form a deep instep notch. Stack the blocks criss-cross to air dry before the cottage clogmaker under-takes the fine paring to the shape of the foot (clogs should be made for individuals, not mass-produced). Cut grooves to hold the leather uppers, sand the wood comfortably smooth and add clog-irons on the sole so that it rocks for easy walking and clacks for clog-dancing.

Turnery

Roundwood is the natural produce of a coppice (in contrast to the sawn produce from timber trees) and turnery is the craft of fashioning roundness on a lathe, be it in the form of a shaped pole or a bowl. A lathe is a device in which an item is rotated at speed on a horizontal axis against the edge of a cutting, gouging or scraping blade held and guided by the worker, so that the wood is gradually whittled to a round or oval shape and can also be grooved around its circumference.

Pole-lathes and bow lathes

The traditional pole-lathe is typical of coppice work in that it is made on the spot by the craftsman who will use it, to a design several centuries old, and is simple in structure but effective. It has a bed, or table, penetrated by two stout, vertical posts (puppets or poppets), one of which is fitted with an iron pin and the other an adjustable screw so that the piece of wood to be worked can be gripped between their points. There is a foot treadle beneath the bed. The characteristic feature of the pole-lathe is the method by which the treadle operates the lathe: a growing sapling or a long, freshly cut pole whippy enough to arch like a longbow under tension and spring back again when released, with its butt end secured to a strong post at ground level, stands with its more slender end high above the lathe (perhaps 12ft). A cord runs from this springy tip down to the lathe, passing a couple of times around the billet of wood waiting to be worked, with its other end fixed to the treadle. As the treadle is pressed down, the tip of the pole is arched downwards and the billet is rotated in one direction; when the treadle is released, the pole flexes back into an upright position again and the billet rotates in the opposite direction. As the treadle is pressed down, a tool blade can be applied to the spinning billet but must be removed each time the treadle is released: the wood cannot be worked when it is turning backwards.

A bow lathe is similar in principle except that the springy pole is replaced by a horizontal bow above the lathe and the cord is attached to the bowstring. It allows for more delicate work but, like a pole-lathe, the blade can only be applied as the treadle is pressed down. In both cases, the tool is rested against a bar while the turner guides the cutting edge by hand against the work.

During the 19th century the problem of alternating rotation was solved by the invention of continuous-direction lathes, driven by a treadle or by an assistant turning a wheel, or by water power or, later, steam and eventually electricity. The basic steps in turning a billet of wood into a turned cylindrical shape are these:

1 Use a hatchet or plane to knock off the corners so that the wood is roughly rounded.
2 Set it between the lathe's chucks (the points on the poppets), balanced on an axis through the centre of the length of the wood.
3 As the wood spins on the lathe, hold a large gouge with its cutting edge just skimming the work until it is more or less round in cross-section, then use chisels, moving them from side to side along the whole length to create the shaping and size you require. For further embellishment, you can hand-carve it when you have finished turning it.
4 Sand, wax and polish the piece while it is still on the lathe.

It sounds quite simple, doesn't it? Don't believe it!

Bodgery

Some of the coppice crafts already described use a rough form of turnery but without the aid of a lathe. Perhaps the best example of a traditional woodland turner is the bodger, an itinerant craftsman whose temporary camp and workshop were once familiar in the coppices around the Chilterns furniture-making town of High Wycombe. Bodgers bought stands of trees, especially beech, and converted them into chair legs; they were almost the forerunners of John Makepeace (a supreme example of a creative user of roundwood) in that they took the process all the way from selecting the growing raw material and converting it into a finished product. They chose individual trees, felled them themselves, sawed the trunks into carefully measured butts, split them with beetle and wedges, trimmed the triangular billets into more or less pentangular lengths with tapered ends (using side-axes), refined the shape a little further by shaving it with a two-handled drawknife and then turned their wood on pole-lathes into all manner of patterned chair legs, using a range of chisels and gouges to carve their designs. They also turned rods for the backs of Windsor or stickback chairs (a style produced towards the end of the 17th century) and the stretchers to brace them; but the actual putting together of the chair and the fashioning of its seat, back bow, splat and armbows, though originally a bodger's work, were generally carried out by other craftsmen in town workshops and factories as the old country craft became the basis of mass production.

Stools and chairs

It is probable that the basic concept of a Windsor chair, i.e. turned sticks driven into a solid seat, arose from that most rustic piece of furniture, the three-legged stool which, as every housecow milker knows, is much more stable on an uneven cowhouse floor than a four-legged seat. It can also be more readily pivoted out of harm's way in a hurry by the sitter. Three-legged cottage chairs were once quite common, too — good solid pieces of very simple design and manufacture. While most cottage floors today have no need of three-legged seating, hand-milkers still appreciate three-legged stools and sturdy ones can be quite hard to find unless you make them yourself — for yourself or for other hand-milkers. No doubt you can think of other users and of ways of embellishing the basic piece of furniture if stool-making appeals to you as a cottage industry.

Milking stools

You need a thick slab of wood for the seat: elm is ideal if you can find some because it resists splitting and warping. You also need three turned legs. The stool described here is essentially rustic in appearance but you can refine the finishing if you want a more sophisticated piece.

Use a saw (bow or large coping) to convert the slab into a disc and then round off its edges with a drawknife. Optionally, you can gouge out the centre of the seat to form a comfortable depression but leave a margin of about 5 cm around the edge.

Mark the positions for the legs: set the point of a compass on the rim, adjust it to a radius equal to that of the seat and mark the two points where the compass line meets the rim, set the compass on them to mark more points and so on — you will end up with six points marked. Divide the disc into thirds by drawing a radius to every alternate point from the centre: these are the lines along which to set the three legs, at perhaps 7 cm from the edge of the seat. They will be splayed rather than vertical so that you need to drill holes for them at a slight angle. Make the holes all the way through the thickness of the seat and slightly smaller than the leg diameter.

Little by little, taper the tops of the legs slightly so that they can be pushed into the holes with their tops flush with the top of the seat and no further. When you have achieved a good 'push fit', remove them and cut out a notch in the tapered end before pushing them back into place, then tamp wedges into the notches from above to expand the leg across the grain of the seat — you can add glue to the wedges for good measure. Trim off any wedge protrusions so that the seat is flush and trim off the ends of the legs so that the stool stands square to the floor.

Chairs

In medieval times, turners progressed from stools to all sorts of chairs using turned elements in the backs and arms as well as the legs. You can use turnery to make everything from spindlebacks and kitchen ladderbacks to rocking chairs, and you can create something more elaborate than cottage chairs if you are prepared to use wood bending and carving techniques as well.

Bentwood chair with perforated wooden seat.

For a Windsor chair, you need a slab of elm about 2 in thick, fashioned with an adze into the traditionally comfortable saddle shape (the art was known as bottoming for good reason). The adze works against the grain: its horizontal blade is set at right angles to the long handle and it is swung to and fro rather like a field mattock, with both hands, as you stand over the wood and spoon out shavings of timber.

Drill holes into the seat to take the back rods (each at precisely slightly different angles) and the splayed legs. Insert the turned legs temporarily so that you can mark the positions of the stretchers and drill holes for them in the legs; traditionally there are three, two in parallel to join front legs to back legs on each side and the third as a brace between them across the middle. When you are satisfied with the fit, assemble and glue legs and stretchers at their joints and then tamp and wedge the legs into their seat-holes, sawing and chiselling the stubs flush with the seat.

The Windsor is either bow-backed, with a steam-shaped hoop framing the spokes, or simply comb-backed like a typical kitchen chair with a gentle curve to the setting of the rails and their 'comb' of solid wood along the top. Bows are usually of cleft ash or perhaps beech, oak, yew or fruitwoods: a four-foot cleft billet is roughly trimmed with a drawknife before being steamed and shaped around a former to set in a 'U'. In due course its two ends are temporarily placed in their seat holes so that the positions of the spokes can be marked against the bow and their receiving holes drilled into it. The spokes usually go right through the bow and are trimmed off later. Sometimes the central spoke is a flat splat with a fretsaw design cut into it and often there are bracing sticks to strengthen the back, set into a protruding 'bobtail' tongue on the seat. Finally the wood is smoothed and then stained, varnished, painted or polished.

Bentwood chairs can be quite cheap and cheerful: you need to understand steaming and shaping techniques to form the hooped back and the gently curved legs. The seat itself has a circular frame which is sometimes filled with a disc of perforated wood instead of traditional rushwork or cane. The chair can be polished, varnished or perhaps painted in kitchen colours for fun.

Bowls

The woodsman's pole-lathe was also used for generations to turn domestic items such as bowls. Village turners produced countless wooden spoons, ladles, platters, rolling pins, pestles and mortars, mangle rollers, cheese vats, lacemaking bobbins, butter-making utensils, egg cups, jars, mugs and so on, usually of sycamore — a white wood which does not stain or taint food — or perhaps beech or alder. Later, those living near towns began to turn wooden parts for factory machines (especially birch bobbins and spools) and more elaborate furniture legs and bedposts, often built up from several different pieces of wood glued together before being turned, but it is for 'treen' that country craftsmen will best be remembered. The word means, literally, 'of the trees', but is generally applied to domestic wooden items smaller than furniture, some of them very simple and utilitarian, others elaborately carved after turning. Table 1 (overleaf) suggests just a few of the wide range of items that can be made by turners, carvers and other woodworkers.

The turner's lathe, even a simple pole-lathe, can produce hollow vessels as well as solid cylinders like chair legs, but the art and the tools used are slightly different. Bowls are produced from solid butts, seasoned for at least several months before being worked; they are roughly shaped with a side-axe to form the outside of the bowl, then rounded further with a drawknife or gouge. The face is then secured to a mandrel on the lathe and the pole cord is wound round the mandrel rather than round the wood. Modern lathes have woodscrews to hold the block of wood to a faceplate mounted on the drive spindle.

The outside is turned first, initially with a rough gouge and then a chisel, making sure that the bowl's base is shaped so that it will stand true on a flat surface. The inside is

TABLE 1

Working with Wood

Egg cups	Carved spoons	Carved figures	Painted furniture
Salt pots	Loving cups	Mechanical figures	Oriental furniture
Soup bowls	Butterprints	Mobiles	Country dressers
Napkin rings	Biscuit stamps	Signposts	Church furniture
Ink pots	Seals	Fingerplates	Parquet floors
Mugs, goblets	Puzzles	Cottage latches	Antique restoration
Potpourri bowls	Toys	Cottage windows	Musical instruments
Fruit bowls	Farmyards	Architectural	Cuckoo clocks
Rolling pins	Forts	mouldings	Barometers
Spice jars	Decoy ducks	Carved bargeboards	Candelabra
Wooden spoons	Carved sticks	Panelling	Crosses
Pepper mills	Croquet sets	Relief carving	Christmas cribs
Thimbles	Pub games	Log boxes	Picture frames
Soup bowls	Board games	Coal scuttles	Mirror frames
Salad bowls	Loo seats	Well buckets	Veneer
Platters	Puppets	Barrels	Marquetry
Doorknobs	Rockinghorses	Flower tubs	Longbows
Light pulls	Ride-ons	Butter churns	Crossbows
Wooden eggs	Figureheads	Mangers	Painted trays
Bud vases	Swings	Spinningwheels	Carved trays
Bobbins	Seesaws	Hand looms	Exccutive toys
Shoe horns	Carousels	Garden totempoles	Model boats
Paperknives	Cricket bats	Garden furniture	Boatbuilding
Yoyos, tops	Tool handles	Rocking chairs	Bridges
Candlesticks	Club shields	Bobbin chairs	Wagons, carts, traps
Skittles	Heraldry panels	Windsor chairs	Wheelwrighting
Table lamps	House signs	Milking stools	Well-heads
Chesspieces	Chopping boards	Carved stools	Dolls' houses
Butter dishes	Bread boards	Bentwood chairs	Model villages
Nutcrackers	Carving boards	Shaker furniture	Carved animals
Letter openers	Carved bellows	Children's chairs	Chainsaw carving
Flutes	Book-ends	Carved chests	Moving toys
Bannisters	Rulers	Blanket boxes	Ethnic toys
Newel posts	Boxes	Trestle tables	Noah's Ark
Bed posts	Pillarboxes	Coffee tables	Rocking pigs
Pipe bowls	Snuffboxes	Games tables	Airplanes
Carved pencils	Cigarette boxes	Animal furniture	

gradually cut away from its outer edge towards the centre and the last slender core of wood is cut out by hand with a knife before the bowl's surface is finely smoothed and polished. Traditional bowl-turners use special hooked knives with curved blades, rather like a grapefruit knife, and skilled workers can make the most of their wood by producing several nesting bowls from a single block. They can also make beakers, goblet and mugs (fix a stop to make sure that a section remains uncut so that it can be carved to form a handle later).

Today the lathes of cottage turners are less crude than the bodger's pole-lathe and there is huge scope for producing beautifully turned articles in a wide variety of wood. I am the proud possessor of a set of caressable bowls in English woods like cherry, walnut, apple, yew and box, with some matching turned ornaments that show off the gorgeous colours and patterns of the different woods,

TURNERY WOODS AND TOOLS

The section of wood in the foreground reveals the pattern of the birch log (seen in the background) which is in the early stages of decay. On the right: the initial stages of converting a square block into a rounded shape.

Bowls: Beautiful examples of the turner's art, in cherrywood.

Turned ornaments in beech, cherry and walnut.

produced by a local turner who has the imagination and skill to exploit the grain of the raw material to best advantage. The understanding and revelation of the grain is an art which can never be taught. The pieces delight the eye and are also irresistible to the touch — better than worry-beads any day!

However, these lovely articles cannot be produced by a few quick turns of the lathe, nor can they be mass produced. To be a successful wood turner you need an innate feel for wood, a sound training in the necessary skills and a great deal of patience and experience. But the scope, once you are lured by the lathe, is considerable.

Whittling and carving

Whittling is for fun, sitting in the sun with a knife and a stick and letting your imagination take charge of your hand, but carving is more serious: skill, an artist's eye and experience are needed and the creative possibilities are unlimited. Finding a market for carved wares, however, is quite another matter.

Carving techniques

Even for fairly simple carving, you need to invest in quite a few tools. A typical set accumulated over the years might include up to fifty assorted chisels, gouges and knives of different sizes and different cutting angles, and even a beginner needs at least half a dozen chisels and gouges, several rasping and finishing tools, a woodcarver's mallet, a carpentry set (saws, planes, drills), a good workbench and clamps and — very important — sharpeners to keep the tools well honed.

Apart from turnery, the main carving techniques are *chip carving*, which is decoration by nicking out small chips with simple tools — the basis of much ethnic carving but far from primitive: *adze and knife work* to form three-dimensional reliefs on symbolic pieces such as totem poles and masks; *flat chisel and round gouge work* seen typically in fairly rough reliefs in medieval churches; and *drilled and pierced work*, a later and more elaborate technique, especially in architecture for wall panels, staircases, door posts, furniture and so on, often with ornate representations of fruit, foliage, birds and animals — florid and flamboyant in the style of Grinling Gibbons or more delicate fretsaw-and-stencil pieces.

Then there are the decorative applications of pieces of different woods and other materials (such as shells, mastic and metals) to cover up a more common wood. For *inlay* work, a flat recess is gouged and chiselled out to a marked pattern and then individual blocks of decorative woods are cut very precisely to the pattern until the jigsaw puzzle makes a tight fit and stands slightly proud. Each block is cut so that its visible face shows across or with the grain but never to display the end grain. The pieces are glued and tapped home, sanded level and then polished and waxed. For *marquetry*, fine sheets of wood (all of equal thickness) are cut into shapes and bedded in glue on the base ply board without recessing. You can buy various wood veneers in thin sheets all ready to be cut, glued and pressed for a couple of days (cover with newspaper — the pieces are delicate) before being finely glasspapered and polished.

Tunbridgeware is, or was, an oddly local craft in Kent which was used to embellish little boxes, tabletops, picture frames, games boards, toys, platters and so on. It is effectively the mass production of wooden mosaic motifs. Use planks 100cm long, 20cm wide and 5mm thick and cut them from side to side in slices 5mm wide so that you have wooden rods 5mm × 5mm × 20cm. Colour the rods variously, then bundle and glue together combinations of colours according to your mosaic pattern (their ends reveal the pattern). Wrap each bundle in newspaper and clamp it until the glue has set, then slice it across finely (1cm thick if you can) like a loaf of bread so that the pattern is reproduced in each slice. Glue the mosaics to the base surface, pad with newspaper and press.

Use your imagination. For example, take a plain white wood like sycamore, dye it in lots of unexpected colours and glue them together in thin laminated sheets like liquorice allsorts, then machine the wood into boxes, plates, bowls, ornaments, jewellery, pillar boxes . . .

Toys

Toys can be turned (beech and hornbeam are commonly used) or made entirely by carving and carpentry. There seems to be a growing market for well-produced wooden toys — trains and other wheeled toys, puppets, animals, toy houses, puzzles, spinning tops, yoyos. Here again, use your imagination to create something original and perhaps designed more as a beautiful item for an adult than as a plaything for a child.

Smallholders might appositely make traditional wooden farmyards including buildings, fencing, animals and model tractors, perhaps. (My earliest memory of a favourite toy was a farmyard with realistic lead animals — much more weighty and satisfying than plastic even if they were dangerous!) The scope for model-making in wood is of course enormous, from matchsticks to tree trunks, and for adults as well as children. Who knows? Your handmade toys of today might become collector's items and the antiques of tomorrow. Make them well! And if you have the delicate touch and the eyesight, think what can be done with dolls houses . . .

Music

Beautiful wooden musical instruments such as violins, mandolins and lutes are very much for the specialist craftworker. You can check for details of courses at places like West Dean College (see Appendix) but it will take many years to acquire sufficient skills. However, you could try something much more simple like whistles and pipes. The easiest recorder, which we used to make as seven-year-old children, was a stout length of bamboo with a slanted cut at the top to take a cork mouthpiece: the skill was to drill the finger holes in the right places and of the right size to produce a scale of notes, and the music could be delightful (especially from a distance across a field!). Panpipes are in effect a series of recorders without finger holes: the different notes are made by different lengths of pipe bound together in a row — try hollow elder tubes or reedstems. Whistles can be made from hollow elder, reeds, or the tip of an animal's horn with a dried pea to make the whistle warble.

House-signs

As a cottage industry, this has obvious scope. You can carve lettering into the wood and add suitable embellishments; you can use wood-burning techniques, applying a hot iron to etch and scorch the letters rather than simply acting as a brush-wielding sign painter; you can shape the sign itself with carving techniques appropriate to the house or use naturally shaped log slices or driftwood (though there are more pleasingly decorative uses for wood shaped and smoothed by water); or you could use completely different materials like glazed clay or wrought metal. Keep thinking: a lot of people live in houses.

Furniture

Furniture-making based on joinery rather than the turned cottage stools and chairs already considered is a craft worthy of long apprenticeship and beyond the scope of this book. There are several unusual training centres, for example John Makepeace's school in Dorset and the West Dean College in Sussex if you are interested in original techniques and concepts. There is also ample scope for original ideas such as animal-shaped furniture for children, perhaps, or painted cottage furniture decorated with stencilwork. Look to the rich traditions of eastern Europe for inspiration.

The Rural Development Commission, which has supplanted the familiar CoSIRA (Council for Small Industries in Rural Areas), issues full working drawings of a good range of traditional furniture including chairs, tables, chests, cabinets, torcheres, dressing tables, wardrobes, dressers, cane-back settees, garden benches, stools, sideboards, bookcases, desks, church furniture and spinning wheels. Rocking chairs but no rocking horses . . .

Start with something reasonably simple like a good, solid trestle table. The originals were simply two trestles with loose cleftwood boards laid across them: the boards were so thick and heavy that their own weight kept them in place and they needed no central support. A complete tree trunk was split in half with wedges, then sliced into boards 2–4 in thick with the aid of an adze (the discarded outer slabwood found a use as cladding for livestock housing). Where now can you find those old, scrubbed kitchen trestle tables on which pastry was rolled and vegetables were chopped in pre-Formica days? They were nicked and scored but infinitely more full of character . . .

Cooperage

The word coop, in this context, has its roots in the Latin word for a cask, hence a cooper is one who makes casks, tubs, vats, barrels and firkins — and also pails, buckets, churns, water carriers or other wooden ware designed to hold liquids, and casks for other goods such as butter, herrings, flour and a wide range of dry commercial cargo goods. They often worked in towns but rural coopers, although they were often also wheelwrights and perhaps the village carpenter and turner producing all sorts of domestic ware, found most of their day-to-day work in endless domestic tubs and buckets — for washing, for salting, for mixing dough, or butter churns and other dairy implements like milking pails, cheese vats and butter washers, or small, portable firkins and harvest kegs to carry field-workers' refreshments. As a natural extension to making casks, coopers made all kinds of hoops — including those for children to bowl. Today, perhaps, the main outlet for cottage coopers is in ornamental garden tubs, with greater individuality than the mass-produced ranges so often seen in mail-order catalogues, but those with imagination will find other uses for the basic coopering technique.

Most cooperage vessels consist of riven staves bound by tightly fitting wooden or iron hoops, with dowelled boards cut into circles to form base and lid. Oak is the traditional wood for casks to hold liquids (especially alcoholic), the sizes of which have to be precise in that they are designed to prescribed capacities. The art of so-called wet cooperage is to make the casks water-tight without the aid of glue, caulk or any other sealants: it is the closeness of fit between adjoining pieces of wood that retains the liquid.

'Dry' containers were often of softwood bound with hazel hoops, or of whatever wood was locally available, but containers for dairywork and kitchen tubs were of 'white' woods (especially sycamore) to avoid staining or tainting their contents.

Wet cooperage is the more difficult craft, of course. Staves are split out from logs of appropriate length cut from oak heartwood; they must then be carefully shaped on both faces so that the inside is made slightly concave with a hollowing knife and the outside convex with a backing knife. The long edges of the stave are chiselled with a sideaxe so that it is broadest across its middle and tapers slightly towards each end, with the edges bevelled for a snug fit against neighbouring staves in due course. At this stage, note that the staves are in a level plane: if they are all propped upright in a circle, only their fat waists will touch each other and the overall shape is a vertical cylinder. The familiar bulging shape of a barrel is achieved by binding the staves with their hoops while they have been rendered pliable by steaming, and the initial shaping of the individual staves allows for this bending by the pressure of the hoops.

That initial dressing of the staves is the most important part of the work, especially for wet coopering. Not only must each stave be correctly shaped in preparation for binding but the bevelling must be at angles which are exactly radial to the centre of the barrel. The angling depends on the final circumference of the barrel and the number of staves incorporated into it, and it is judged entirely by eye.

The dressed staves are set upright in a circle with their tops encircled by an iron band (the 'raising-up' hoop) so that they form something like a lampshade shape. Then a large, temporary truss-hoop (originally of cleft ash) can be hammered downwards over the staves to hold them together while they are made pliable, either by steaming or by soaking them and then heating them over wood shavings smouldering in a cresset to dry the inside faces and enable truss-hoops of successively smaller diameter to be driven over the staves, gradually squeezing them toegther in a tight fit from top to bottom until a second iron band can be fitted at the base to hold the cask until its shape has set. The two iron bands and all the truss-hoops are temporary binders whose role is to form the shape of the barrel.

The 'heads' (lid and base) are made from oak planks dowelled together and caulked where they abut each other, then cut to form a circle of appropriate diameter with its rim bevelled to fit a groove cut into the inside face of the staves after their ends have been levelled off with an adze and plane and the rim bevelled along its inside edge. The heads must be measured precisely to fit the grooves.

While the heads and the grooves are being prepared, the cask will have set its shape and the truss-hoops can be removed so that the surface of the vessel can be made smooth with the concave blade of a down-right shave. A tapered bung-hole can be bored into the barrel if required. Temporary hoops are again put in place around the middle of the barrel and the two iron end bands are removed to allow the heads to be manoeuvred into place. Finally, the cask is ready for its permanent hoops, measured to fit exactly: iron bands are rivetted into circles tapered to correspond with the cask's shape before they are hammered down to fit tightly — two or three at each end, depending on the size of the cask, and with their overlap joints on opposite sides to avoid distortion.

Dry barrels need not be built quite so accurately: sometimes referred to as 'slack' barrels, they are not necessarily watertight. They are bound with cleft hazel rods (with the bark intact) steamed into pliability for forming into hoops, or formed while still green, and secured with clenched nails. Otherwise the method of assembly is similar to that for wet casks except that only one head is fitted, at the base; the other is a lid to be put in place once the barrel is full and can be kept in place for transport by hammering down the top hoop to tighten the staves around it.

'White' cooperage for dairyware and domestic use is based on similar principles again except that tubs, churns and buckets only taper at one end so that the staves are much simpler to dress. Today people use adhesive tape to hold the staves together temporarily in a flat plane, rather like a length of chestnut paling fence, and then literally wrap them around the base (having cut a groove beforehand) and glue the whole lot together. The hoops, whether metal or hazel, thus become merely decorative. Typical cottage-made white cooperage includes well-buckets, feed buckets, coal scuttles, flower tubs and plunger butter-churns, which are narrower at the top than the base, and straight-sided in contrast to the more sophisticated end-over churn, which is cask-shaped but without an exaggerated belly.

Economically-minded settlers found ways of recycling their damaged barrels by converting them into furniture, especially barrel chairs, the origins of which could be concealed under upholstery.

Wheels, wagons and barrows

Wheelwrighting and wagon building or renovation are really beyond the capabilities of most cottage industrialists or smallholders unless there is a family tradition or a local craftsman looking for a long-term apprentice but, who knows, you might be so inspired by the sheer beauty of what used to be so commonplace that you will be willing to commit yourself to the crafts.

Wheelwrighting

The strains and thrusts imposed on the wheel of a cart are considerable and complex. A spoked wooden wheel is carefully designed to a high standard of engineering in order to withstand such stresses: a dished wheel, with its spokes slanting inwards to the hub from the rim, is many times stronger than a flat wheel and its load-bearing capacity is increased if it is set at an angle to its load so that the dished spokes are at right angles to the ground surface as their section of rim touches the road.

The hub (or nave, or stock) is of the heartwood of a split-resisting species such as elm, seasoned perhaps five or ten years. It needs to be strong enough to remain resilient although much of the wood is cut away: there is a large hole for the axle, with a cast-iron bearing or box fitted into it, and numerous slots for the spokes. After being roughly hewn to shape with axe or adze, the hub is turned on a large lathe into a barrel or cylindrical shape, with recesses for the iron hoops that will encompass its ends. An average cartwheel five feet across would have a hub 12–14in in diameter and in depth.

A wheel has an equal number of spokes, from eight to sixteen depending on its size, and always of seasoned cleft oak heartwood. Each spoke is carefully shaped so that it is more or less ovoid in cross-section (its thicker part towards the inner wheel for strength) with a square or round peg-like tongue to fit into the rim slot and a tapered foot for the carefully angled hub mortices. The spokes are hammered into the hub before the tongues are created with tenon saw and chisel.

The rim is in segments or felloes, usually one to every two spokes, made from ashwood and joined together with dowels of cleft oak heartwood an inch in diameter. After the felloes have been fitted to the spokes (no easy task), the protruding spoke tongues are levelled off and the flush ends are wedged.

Many a village pond has played a role in subsequent wheel maintenance when the wood has shrunk and loosened the wheel's components: a good, long soak swells them back to a tight fit again.

Finally the rim is shod protectively with iron, either in sections nailed on so that they overlap the felloe joints or in a continuous band to form a hoop tyre, made and set by a blacksmith and applied hot so that the metal contracts to a good fit as it is rapidly cooled with water before the wood can burn.

Carts and wagons

Whole books have been written on the intriguing regional variations of two-wheeled farm carts and four-wheeled wagons which have been so comprehensively displaced by tractor-drawn and factory-made trailers and by juggernaut lorries. James Arnold's books, among others, are magnificent, with superb drawings which reveal every detail of harvest wagons, hermaphrodites, trolleys, drays, spring carts, boat-wagons, barge-wagons, straight-beds, crooked-beds, waisted-beds, tipcarts, scotch carts, butt carts, moss carts, box carts, woad carts, tumbrels, dobbin carts, ladder wains, kerry carts, sledges, tumblers, gambos . . . and that is only the rural traffic.

They are hardly likely to be seen on our roads and farms again in any number, though there does seem to be a return in towns to old-fashioned tradesmen's delivery vehicles and of course the crowds all love the big-horse parades when resplendent wagons come into their full glory. If you are interested in renovating or even making carts and wagons as a cottage industry, you have a great deal to learn, not just about their structure but also about colours. Every region had its preferences for different tints of different colours — Prussian blue, Brunswick blue, Saxe blue, indigo, greens galore, Venetian red, Crimean red, scarlet, claret, orange, ochre, brown, chrome yellow, lime yellow, buff, cream, white — different colours for different parts of the vehicle's outside, interior, wheels, panelling, grooves, undercarriage and lettering, even for farm wagons.

In a Hampshire village not far from my own in Sussex, there is a man whose parents were of gipsy stock and who has been a coachbuilder for more than thirty years. Peter Ingram bought his first caravan when he was 15 but it was much later that he set up his unique Romany folk museum and workshop at Limes End Yard, where he renovates gipsy caravans and showman's vans. The museum has a collection of brilliantly coloured canal-boat artefacts and gipsy clothes as well as vans. As a child I used to play and sleep in a slowly rotting wooden van with peeling blue paint which stood rather forlornly in a meadow, the weeds tangling themselves through its wheels and binding it to its final resting place, though in my dreams it was bright and alive, rolling on squeaking wheels behind a skew-bald horse along the lanes. But, somehow, it seems unlikely that revulsion against the pollution and murderous potential of the combustion engine will bring back the more leisurely and far less dangerous days of real horsepower on the motorways . . .

However, many smallholders devise light two-wheeled carts to be drawn by the family donkey, goat, sheep or ox. For example, a shay or sulky for a racing donkey (no, that is not necessarily a contradiction in terms!) needs only a couple of bicycle wheels and a simple light frame with a plank-seat across the shafts: the expensive part of the outfit is the harness. The annual Balmoral Show, staged by the Royal Ulster Agricultural Society, features a unique parade of vintage donkey-drawn implements and is a good source of inspiration to those who would like their donkeys and mules to help around the smallholding or take them to the shops. Some of the goat carts seen at shows are quite elaborate and beautifully made.

Barrows

A simple handcart is invaluable on a small-holding or large garden — two spoked wheels (wood if you want to try your hand at wheelwrighting on a small scale, or use old bicycle or pram wheels) on an axle, with a flatbed of timber planks running lengthways, and an extension of the supporting underframe at the end with a bar across as a handle. Attach an old broomstick to the bar by a leather loop: let the stick drop down as a rest-stake when the cart is stationary, or swing it up out of the way to rest its free tip on the flatbed. You could make a detachable carrying box to go on top of the bed and, before you know it, you have progressed to building trailers and horseboxes.

For a more realistic cottage industry, how about handmade wooden wheelbarrows? They have the drawback of being much heavier than a modern metal or plastic barrow but, if properly balanced, are no more laborious to use and infinitely more pleasing to handle and see. Give it a wooden wheel — elm for the hub and ash spokes and felloes; make the underframe and boards of elm or oak and the shafts of ash. In the 1930s R. W. Farman, a Norfolk craftsman working from North Walsham, made pretty little wickerwork wheelbarrows selling at 24 shillings each, carriage paid.

Cabins and sheds

Logs can be turned into two simple essentials: boats and houses. A log raft is too easily made to require description; it does not have to be waterproofed as its buoyancy is innate. A primitive canoe carved from a hollowed log takes much more work and skill. If you really want to stretch yourself and your friends, however, build a log cabin.

Log cabins

The traditional Scandinavian and North American method of building a homestead with the help of a few strong neighbours depends on a site with direct access to ample forests to supply the large amount of raw materials which is needed. It is really a thoroughly wasteful method of using timber for building! However, the principles involved can be extended to much less ambitious rustic buildings like summer-houses, except that the joy of a real log cabin is that the very weight of the logs and the snugness of their fit make the structure self-supporting so that you do not need to

dig post holes or foundations. Here is how a log cabin was built in America in the 19th century.

Fell the trees, butt them, and let your team of oxen (this is 1857!) haul them to the rolling point, one at a time. Lay a foundation of heavy logs flat on the ground, with large flat stones under each corner, and lay sleepers across them for the main floor.

Use handspikes and levers to roll each log up on to skids (pieces of timber with one end on the ground and the other resting on the last log put in place in the wall) and use crotched poles to heave a log up once it reaches about breast height. To keep the house level, turn the logs so that the butt ends (which are of course thicker) can build up a low point.

Hew rough notches near the ends of each log to ensure a snug fit where the logs cross each other at corners and partitions. The lower log is given a 'saddle bearing', scarfed down from the top on each side, to accept

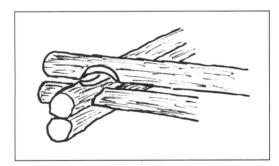

SCARFING JOINTS FOR A LOG CABIN

The notch scooped out of the new pole fits snugly into the saddle scooped out of the pole already in place.

the next log's notch, which is cut to match when it is on site so that the new log can be rolled over into its place with a snug fit. Make sure you keep the corners perpendicular. As you build up the walls, either scarf-mark or cut out areas for doors and windows.

When the first storey is high enough, lay your beams, notched and saddled like other logs. The bearers should be flattened ready to receive the floor of the second storey (if there is one).

Roofing shingles made from carefully split oak.

Gable logs should be carefully scarfed off at the ends to give the desired roof pitch. Rafter logs, laid lengthways, are notched upon the gables. Put up your ridge poles — and that, in theory, completes the first day's labour!

On the following day, cut out the doors and windows if you have not already done so; lay the floors and put on the roof. If you have no floorboards, make 'puncheons' by splitting logs into short planks. For the roof, use boards or newly peeled birch bark with moss: lay the materials lengthways from ridge pole to eaves, with battens, or alternatively, lay thin split-oak staves and hold them firmly in place with poles which have been 'withed' at the ends so that they stay in place and can be firmly pressed down on the staves to make close joints. For a more elegant finish (if you have the skill), make riven oak shingles or shakes — in effect wooden roofing tiles. You need the typical coppice craftsman's equipment and skills to split out the shingles in a cleaving brake with the help of a froe.

Hew down the logs to make indoor wall faces, then lay a clay hearth at one end of the cabin and build a chimney from split timber and clay. And that's it — a house built in two days flat.

Bandsaw mills

In a new age, the cabin builder uses a portable bandsaw mill to turn the logs into lumber and builds rustic houses of seasoned planks and panelling. The bandsaw also helps in making the cabin's furniture. The Wood-Mizer catalogue, published in Indianapolis, includes a photo album of its customers' imaginative build-it-yourself timber homes — simple shedlike shacks with porches (and rocking-chairs), log-style cabins, barns, elaborate tree palaces, multiple dwellings and even a whole recreation centre on an Indian reservation in Canada. They have experimented with different timbers, mixing the colours and grains, and many who started by building their own homes have become so enthusiastic that they have made businesses of log-cabin construction, using their bandsaw mills to make floorboards, wall panels, casements, doors and verandahs, carefully airdrying their timber in the stack before building with it — which is in contrast to the old log cabins made from trees hewn on the same day so that the wood seasoned while it was part of the building.

Sheds

If you are prepared to invest in your own sawmill equipment, whether portable or permanent, or can purchase sawn timber from a local village mill, your horizons are boundless and a 'cottage' industry becomes a cottage building industry. With other smallholders in mind, you could start on a simple basis by designing and making hutches for pets (perhaps for sale to your local pet shop) or affordable livestock housing. The easiest and probably most profitable would be poultry units such as coops, chicken houses and portable arks, with the emphasis on 'affordable'. Take the example of the Ten Hen units built at Framingham Pigot, Norfolk, and devised as cheap, self-assembly starter kits for back-yard egg production (complete with hens): this idea was so successful that within a matter of weeks the range was extended to include a Duck Billet, a Bunny Hut and of course a Dog House, all with interchangeable components and the option to add partitions, legs, runs and so on as required in particular situations.

Other cottage-based industries make affordable bee hives, goat housing, backyard pig huts and simple looseboxes or basic field shelters (three sides and a single-pitch roof). Some customers prefer self-assembly units if they can be put together simply and quickly; others would rather someone else took the responsibility of putting the unit in place, but you might find costing such work a problem. Time is money and travel can be expensive, so that you might price yourself out of the market on the numerous, scattered small jobs which are bound to come your way. There is also the problem of investment in bought-in materials or sawmill equipment, unless you decide to aim at those who are more interested in ornament than practicality — perhaps beautiful garden dovecotes or carpeted kennels for pampered pets, complete with your homemade beanbags. There is a huge potential market in accessories, toys and grooming aids for pets, by the way.

If you are a smallholder, you have the advantage of knowing from experience not only what other smallholders need and can afford but also what designs are best for the welfare of the animals. Make the most of your expertise and your knowledge of animal behaviour, and then sell advice as well as housing. If you can offer very good livestock to go with the units, so much the better. Can you see quite a satisfying little cottage industry building up?

Think ahead: anticipate how problems with commercial food production and storage, animal welfare, set-aside schemes, environmentally sensitive areas and changes in agricultural support and methods might affect the outlook for those who distrust the food they buy for some reason. What practical steps will such people take to ensure that their food is as they want? Backyard egg booms are a direct result of the salmonella scare combined with a dislike of battery systems. What next for the backyarder? What can you build to cater for the new needs?

Woodland byproducts

Bark, wood chippings and other woodland byproducts are increasingly in demand by gardeners seeking alternatives to dwindling peat resources, by stables for gallop surfaces, by those in charge of public areas for pathways and for soft landings in playgrounds, by livestock owners for bedding, and as sources of alternative energy, energy conservation by insulation, and building materials such as fibreboards. You need access to chipping and shredding machines: co-operatives and contractors invest in portable ones and take them to the woodland edge. On a very small scale you might find a way of using a garden compost shredder to produce bagged mulches, or to turn resinated woods into chips for smoking home-produced bacon and fish.

Bark

Bark can be used as a raw material in craftwork and building, as a fibre or as sheeting, or in tanning and dyeing. If the tree species is appropriate, bark is the basis of birdlime (from holly bark macerated in water) or of cork — it is possible, just, to grow cork trees in Britain and if the greenhouse effect lives up to its promises the prospects for a cork crop might improve. The spice, cinnamon, is from the bark of the cinnamon tree and, again, it might be that the species will grow in our climate in due course.

Bark can be harvested at intervals from a living tree if you are careful to leave lifelines in place — do not ring-bark the tree or it will die. Harvest when the cambium is actively dividing (say May/June) so that the bark is loose enough to strip even from an oak. Make a pair of circumferential cuts around the trunk or branch, making sure that you never complete the circles, then use the round, flat, spoonlike chisel blade of a barking iron to make vertical cuts between them so that you can peel the bark off in strips, or in one large piece by easing the blade under the bark to lever it clear. If the bark is for tanning, peel from branches too. Oak is the traditional tannery bark but sweet chestnut is good, too, and it has always been claimed that willow makes a more waterproof leather — largely because of the typical folklore association that the tree itself grows in wet places. Let tannery bark dry for a few weeks by hanging it on poles, then stack it with the outer surface uppermost to avoid losing the tannins which are concentrated on the inner surface.

Barkers used to drain the sap to let firewood dry more quickly and make brighter and quicker burning logs, more cheerful to look at but less heat-giving. Peeled wood dries out more quickly than wood with bark intact but it tends to split, which is not desirable for some uses. Sap, incidentally, is at its peak flow in spring, the ideal time for tapping a birch tree to make birch wine.

Blackthorn bark, macerated in rainwater until it forms a thick black deposit at the bottom of the container, was used to make ink in early medieval times. Let it settle, strain off the water and dry the residue; then mix it with gum from the exudates of a cherry tree and grind it into a powder.

In coppice crafts, where bark is often more of a nuisance than a valued material, it is stripped off with a rinder or drawknife (perhaps fashioned from an old fag-hook blade). Brace the pole in a homemade shaving brake and, working on freshly cut wood so that the sap lubricates the blade, hold the bevelled edge in contact with the pole and draw the blade down towards you with strong, even strokes. The bark will peel off in strips and if you are skilful you might be able to use the same blade to produce thin ribbons of oakwood for spelk baskets, riven from the poles while they are still hot from being boiled.

Birch bark is the traditional material for cladding Scandinavian log cabins and American Indian canoes. The Indians of southern Arizona, as if you needed to know, use the same word *ka-nohwa* (from the Spanish *canoa*) for the boat and for a water trough for livestock — not that there are many boats in the desert homeland of the Papago Indians!

Bark is fibrous, and any fibrous material, whether from plants or from animals, can be spun and turned into ropes, mats and cloth if you have the need, curiosity and patience. You might be able to make some interesting wall coverings, for example. In the Baltic countries, the bark of lime trees was used commercially for fibre: because of the tree's lack of knots, the bark could be removed in long strips and macerated in water until the fibrous layers separated. These were divided into narrow slips or 'bass' and plaited into ropes, then woven into mats as containers for exported flax and hemp, or in the garden for covering tender plants or as plant-ties. Juniper bark also used to be quite popular for making ropes. The section on vegetable fibres such as hemp and flax explains principles which can equally be applied to bark fibres. Oakum, incidentally, has nothing to do with oak: it is made from old tarred ropes, teased out and used to caulk the seams of sailing ships.

Leaves and nuts

Nuts are not only edible as nuts but can be useful sources of oil, especially walnut and beech. And once upon a time country workers made themselves goggles out of walnut shells if their task merited eye protection. An idea for children dressing up for Hallowe'en?

Leaves, apart from being used as decorative foliage, can be harvested as a source of protein in spring (for humans as well as livestock) or as ingredients for salads and teas, but choose your species with care: hawthorn is particularly valuable. Or make a science of the study of different leafmoulds.

Wood ash

The value of wood ash as a byproduct is too often neglected. For a start it is excellent in the garden as a mineral-rich fertiliser, especially for lawns, potatoes and tomatoes, and a dusting of wood ash under potato tubers as they are planted will protect them from rotting.

Wood ash is the original potash, or potassium carbonate, a powerful alkali which used to be made by lixiviating (leaching) wood ash and then evaporating it in pots to make lye for washing. The potash industry was once a basic community trade: potash burners scavenged for everything burnable, including river weed, old thatch, straw and general refuse, and would also buy wood ash and sell it to soapmakers. The leaching process involves putting the ash in a barrel with soft water, stirring it and draining it off repeatedly until all the soluble salts have dissolved out. The water is boiled off, or filtered through clean straw which can then be burnt off leaving black, crystalline potash. Refiners used to convert the black crystals into white pearl ash. The salts can be used as manure or for cheap earthenware, or can be turned into soap with the addition of fat.

Exudates

The forest is most generous to human beings. Not only does it provide us with raw timber, bark, cork, charcoal, veneer, wood pulp, wood chips, ornamental trees, nuts, berries, seeds and foliage but also a whole host of exudates and chemicals — gums, balsams, lacs, tannins, salicylic acid (essential to aspirins), latex for rubber and derivatives such as turpentine.

Sap is the tree's life-juice, rich in sugars and starch, transporting minerals from the soil to the powerhouse of the leaves. It runs through the living wood — the sapwood. The heartwood, in contrast, is dead, or at least 'retired' to the function of holding up the tree, and tends to accumulate gums and resins.

Sap can be tapped and turned into syrups and sugars (for example, maple) and wines (birch and spruce). Resins have many uses, quite apart from giving Greek wine its distinctive flavour — resins find their ways into plastics and varnishes, for example. A substitute for gum sandarach (from a Moroccan tree) can be made from the resin which oozes from the trunks of old junipers, and is used for varnish or is pulverised to form pounce. Resin from a species like the Norwegian spruce is distilled into turpentine and Burgundy pitch, whereas incisions into larch trees let you extract the raw material for pure Venice turpentine. True oil of turpentine is from a coniferous balsam, originally from the terebinth or resin tree; wood tar (such as Stockholm tar) is a natural bitumen; pitch is the residue from distilled tars, especially from pitch pines, spruce and silver fir.

Unless you are interested in distilling such materials for your own use — perhaps as a herbalist — your most likely application for tree exudates is tapping sap for wine-making or for syrup.

Maple syrup

The real American sugar maple which produces syrup for waffles is *Acer saccharinum*, the rock maple, which grows east of the Mississippi in central and northern states and in Canada. Its saccharine is stored in the form of insoluble starch, which becomes soluble sugar when the sap begins to flow after the winter frosts. The maximum flow rates are on warm days following freezing nights. The variety does not appear to grow well in Britain but in fact most maples are tappable, though their juice is not as sweet and palatable. The sap-collecting season in Britain is brief, lasting perhaps three weeks in early spring just as the leaf buds break.

The following 19th-century sap-collecting techniques could also be used on birch, tapped in coldish, windy weather during March for three or four weeks — seal the hole again with a wooden bung and wax when you have finished.

Make an augur about half an inch in diameter, with a galvanised metal spout, and insert it near the base of the tree: bore a tapping hole no more than three-quarters of an inch deep and the same in diameter on the south side of the tree. (If the weather is too cold to encourage the sap, it will not even flow on the warmer south face.) The spout could alternatively be cut from an elder twig about 6–8in long with the pith removed or use a 12in length of 1in × 1in

SAP-TAPPING SPIGOTS
One elder twig can be cut to form two spouts.

pine with its upper half removed to within 2in of one end and bore a quarter-inch hole through the remaining thick part with a groove from the hole to the other end. The advantage of a metal spout is that it will be strong enough to hang a bucket on. The collecting bucket or trough, however, should be made of wood.

Use only one spout on a small tree, or two or three on a larger one. Leave the spout in place all season: the bark will probably callous around it during the summer. Collect the sap daily, or it will go sour, and you must also process it on the same day. Make a fire on bare ground and boil up the sap in a shallow cauldron standing on bricks or stones over the flames. Skim off the scum and keep adding fresh sap until the brew is sufficiently concentrated, then reduce the heat and stir the syrup continuously. When it is thick enough to set readily on the spoon (hard, waxy and a little brittle), remove the container from the fire and let the syrup cool so that it crystallises into almost white maple sugar.

2   Basketry and Thatch

Picture this. Christmas, 1930: R. W. Farman of North Walsham, Norfolk, established 'many centuries', offers for sale a wide range of articles made from locally grown osiers and reeds — bird tables with woven rooves, wickerwork wheelbarrows, osier hurdles, basket-chairs, elaborately woven willow and rush tables, rush-seated stools, reed mats to disguise ugly iron or felt rooves, thatched dog kennels and summer-houses, and baskets in every conceivable shape and size.

Or this. Summer, 1990: Jenny Crisp of Stourbridge, West Midlands, designs and makes osier baskets from a crop of willow she has personally planted (on a third of an acre in Devon), harvested by hand, and stripped manually through an old iron stripper or carefully dried of its sap with the beautiful bark intact. She has known every rod that she uses since it first sprouted in the withy bed: she takes her product right through from planting to point of sale, just as traditional basketmakers always used to do.

Willows are the most widely used family of trees for basketry (though thin ribbons of oak can be woven too) and other waterside plants like reeds and rushes are good for woven work. The stems of large grasses and the straw of cereal plants can be plaited or bound and coiled to form baskets and hats; indeed, cereal straw, too often a waste product on the farm, can be a most valuable commodity, woven in hats, matting, paper and ropes or fashioned into ornaments and furniture. In addition, straw has insulating and absorbent properties (it is used as animal litter, insulation board, stuffings, packing material), it is a source of energy (animal feed, boiler fuel) and it has always been used in the vital role of putting a dry roof over human and livestock heads as

thatch, along with reeds, heather and other local materials. Basketry has also played an important part in traditional house-building; whole houses have been made of wicker-work, and what is wattle if not basketry?

Table 2 (opposite) describes some of the wide range of applications for straw, reed, rushes and withies — the main materials considered in this chapter. You will also find

Baskets.

plenty of inspiration by looking at ethnic products from all over the world and adapting the techniques and concepts: if you cannot afford a year or two wandering through South America and the Caribbean, Africa or Indonesia, China and southern Asia, take an armchair wander through an Oxfam catalogue, perhaps, to open your eyes to the endless adaptability of the materials. You can be equally imaginative in your choice of materials: look around the garden, fields, hedgerows and coppices for unusual weavables. The main techniques with these materials are basket-weaving, flat weaving, plaiting, bind-and-coil, cane seating and rush seating, and thatching.

Wicker and withy

The Old English word *wican* means 'to bend' and *withig* is willow. Essentially, a wicker is a pliant rod used in basketry, usually of willow but you can make baskets from all manner of flexible rods including simple hedgerow baskets of dethorned bramble vines or split rowan, ash, poplar and other amenable twiggery. Withies, however, are flexible rods of willow, especially

osier willows which are broadly any willow species used in basketry but usually *Salix viminalis*, the common osier, though *Salix triandra* (the basket willow) is less coarse and a better species for basket rods 6–10 ft long. *Salix purpurea* is sometimes cut for thin rods up to 4 ft long but the widespread goat willow (*Salix caprea*) is too brittle for basketry and the name of the crack willow (*Salix fragilis*) speaks for itself. A good basket willow like osier is pliable when moist but it sets firmly into the woven shape when dry.

Willows are cultivated as a regularly harvested crop for basket-makers. If you are serious about wickerwork or withy baskets, it is only worth growing your own willow if you live in the right part of the country. Nearly all the commercial osier crop now comes from the wetlands of the Somerset Levels where conditions are ideal, though smaller growers in coastal areas supply the local demand for lobster creels and fish traps.

TABLE 2
Straw, Rush, Cane and Osier Ideas

STRAW	RUSH/REED	Chairs	Bird cages
Archery targets	Rushlights	Tables	Lampshades
Mattresses	Reed plaster	Wheelbarrows	Ducknest bottles
Truckle beds	Thatch	Shelves	Hen laying-nests
Briquettes	Table mats	Dressers	Dung skeps
Heat heaps	Floor mats	Carriage panels	Malting skeps
Straw brooms	Chair seats	Stools	Screens
Thatch	Mattresses	Coracles	Wittle bags
Ropes	Hats	Building ramps	Donkey panniers
Halters	Bags	Path protection	Laundry baskets
Screens	Satchels	Swamp hurdles	Bread baskets
Doors	Hassocks	Boat ramps	Egg baskets
Marquetry	Foot stools	Lampshades	Log baskets
Paper	Platters	Houses	Shopping baskets
Corn dollies	Pith ornaments	Window blinds	Garden baskets
Rick finials	Log baskets	Cradles, cribs	Bicycle baskets
Ornaments	Plant pots	Knights' shields	Washing baskets
Models	Cradles		Cat/dog baskets
Beehive chairs	Chairs	BASKETS	Market baskets
Bonnets	Grain baskets	Creels	Fruitshop platters
Cow jackets	Shopping baskets	Eel traps	Trugs
Lamb jackets	Reed boats	Fish kiddles	Spelks
Horse millinery		Balloon baskets	Wiskets
Boaters	CANE/OSIER	Hampers	Punnets
Sunhats	Chair seats	Beehives	

Willows are grown in very good agricultural soil which is well watered by occasional flooding but also well drained so that the water is always fresh rather than stagnant. The stools are set from cuttings about a foot long, pushed into the ground to three-quarters of their length and initially about 35 cm apart in rows 65 cm apart. The first harvest is taken when the plants are three years old and thereafter the new rods which spring readily from the stool can be harvested annually for up to perhaps thirty years, until the stools and the soil are exhausted.

Harvesting is generally in autumn and winter and you can use a billhook (with an upward cut), a reaping hook or a heavy sickle. *Green* willow for lobster creels and fish traps is cut in summer and used fresh, but for most other purposes winter-cut osiers are seasoned and then soaked for use.

Brown willow is woven with its bark intact, as harvested, after being seasoned in loose bundles in a dry, airy place. It is best suited for outdoor use — fish baskets, agricultural carriers, garden furniture and underwater applications, for example.

Buff willow is boiled with the bark intact so that it dyes the wood naturally and then the bark can be removed. Boil the rods in a tank for several hours, then leave them to soak in the same water for a while before stripping off the bark and letting them dry in the fresh air. They must be dry before being stored or there will be problems with mildew, though it is claimed that the boiling produces a stronger rod less susceptible to fungi and rot — and that the boiling process kills off potentially damaging invertebrates and that the tannin impregnation will protect against future attacks.

White willow is stripped of its bark, either immediately after harvesting if the timing is late enough for the sap to be flowing or by 'pitting' immediately after harvest: stand the rods upright with their butts in a few inches of water until they begin to grow roots in the spring, when the sap will be rising and peeling can take place in, say, April or May. Peeling is traditionally done by hand, pulling each rod butt-end first through a peeling brake with two springy metal blades set in a V shape, but today the stripping is usually by mechanical rotary blades.

There used to be many regional names for different varieties — Dicky Meadows, Black Maul, Black Spaniard, Black Sally, Clay, Stone, Black and White Newkinds, Brown Hollands, Glibskins, Red Rods, Bents, Yellow Willows, Longskins, Silverskins, Black Tops, Merrin, for example, and in Suffolk they used the term 'sallow' for any soft wood — not just willows but also alder, hazel and birch. Osiers are generally sold in bundles and graded by length rather than thickness, traditionally in ells (each bundle 45 in in circumference at the base), or with a standard girth averaging about 37 in at the base.

To split white or buff rods into thin 'skeins', use a special egg-shaped cleave with three or four fins: start the split at one end of the rod by means of a sharp knife then push the cleave into the split and along the rod to produce three or four triangular strips. Splits are used for finer work.

Before osiers are used for weaving, they should be carefully soaked in cold water until they are pliable. After soaking, lay them to 'mellow' in an unheated place under a damp cover for a couple of hours or more before trying to work them. Only soak and prepare as many as you can use in the next day or two.

Basic basketry

Absolute beginners might like to experiment with something soft like raffia to understand the weaving techniques before trying their hand with wicker or cane. But once the idea grips you, start experimenting: use colour to make your baskets different, dyeing the materials before weaving them, and have fun mixing different colours. Incorporate other materials to vary the texture as well as the colour. Basketry is essentially three-dimensional: dream up unusual shapes — gourds, cones, kidneys, panniers, globes — or try the open diagonal weave of Colombian cundu baskets which are flexible enough to be pushed into different shapes at whim.

Take a look at the very different Colombian palm baskets with their delicate flower patterns or the beautifully light Ethiopian basket sieves (the essence of basketry is lightweight strength). Combine good techniques with good imagination . . . Visit the Crafts Council shop in the Victoria & Albert Museum or the South Bank Craft Centre at London's Royal Festival Hall for inspiration for original baskets and many other crafts.

To make a basic cane or willow round basket, start at the bottom by 'tying the knot' or making an interlaced 'slath' of stout bottom sticks from the butt-ends of some rods. Form a cross by laying four sticks at right angles across three or four others, passing them through central lengthways slits or tying and interlacing them, ready to be gradually fanned out to form the circular base. Use thinner rods (weavers) to bind the slath as you gradually fan out the spokes, spacing them evenly and keeping the weave tight and firm: start with one long weaver and bend it in half round one arm of the cross, then cross its two ends left over right and take them over/under the next arm of the cross, working clockwise; continue in this way over all four arms for two or three circuits. Now separate the bottom sticks into pairs for a round or two and then revert to singles for further weaving as you gradually mould the base into a slightly humped shape (a convex face on the *inside* of the basket) for stability. There are various other patterns you can use at the centre of the base, and some people prefer to use a wooden or plywood base instead, with holes drilled around the edge to take the upright side stakes.

To join in a new weaver, push it in behind the original one and weave it in. When the base is large enough, 'slype' the weaver ends by making slanted cuts so that you can push them through the previous complete round to secure.

Now insert the side stakes. Slype their butt ends (or use a bodkin to make holes in the edge of the base) and then push them *horizontally* into the circumference so that they radiate as spokes in the same plane as

Basketmaker working on the base of a new basket. *(Photo by Anna Oakford)*

the base. Push the ends in about 2 in into the base weave, one side stake on each side of each bottom stick unless the weaving requires an odd number, in which case you need to add an extra stake and space it appropriately later on as you weave.

The next step is to 'prick up': turn each stake upwards at a right angle by bending it sharply over a knifepoint so that it kinks rather than cracks. Hold the stakes upright temporarily with a loose hoop while you 'upset' the basket to define its eventual shape and give it strength by means of three rounds of 'waling'. For this, use from three to six weaving rods which are almost as thick as the side stakes. Slype the butt ends of these waling rods and push the first one into the base, close to an adjacent side stake; push the second one in next to the second side stake, and so on; then weave each rod in front of two stakes and behind the next two, continuing in sequence and carefully pressing the waling rods down over the angle of the upset stakes in the first round so

Willow eel-trap. *(Photo by Anna Oakford)*

Duck-nest basket. *(Photo by Anna Oakford)*

that you make a strong standing edge. Keep the weave tight for a second and third round to prevent the shape from splaying.

The rest of the basket can be woven to whatever pattern you choose (and the choice is a wide one as long as you took the pattern into account when determining the odd or even number of side stakes in the first place). Finish the work with a firm, tidy border to maintain the shape and to weave in the tips of the side stakes.

These basic techniques can apply to round-cane or osier baskets of all shapes and also wickerwork furniture and even houses.

American willow basket

Use split ash for hoops, ribs and handles, and soaked unpeeled willow for the weave. Bend two ash splits into hoops and put one inside the other at right angles: have them of equal size and circular for a hemispherical basket and crossing at the middle, or let the

inner loop (the rim of the basket) be larger for an oval. Start weaving where the two hoops meet. As you progress, insert U-shaped ribs at intervals, radial to the starting point, to maintain the basket's shape: they will be of sufficient sizes according to that shape. Weave the willows among the ribs down the sides until the growing semicircle of weaving reaches the base of the basket towards the lower part of the upright hoop. Now start on the ends of the basket, weaving the willows down the ends and along the base, adding more ribs as needed. Fill empty areas with weaving. Push the willows close together.

Spelks

Spelks, spales or splints are woven like osier baskets except that the weavers (taws) and the stakes (spells) are both of the same material, like the weft and warp of a loom. The material is thin strips of oak and the

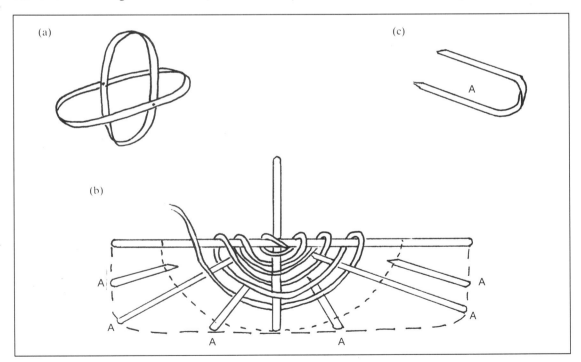

(a) Set hoops at right angles to each other to form the handle and the rim.
(b) Starting the weave. The semicircle is continued until the weave reaches the base of the basket (as shown by the dotted line). Next the ends of the basket are woven and then the remaining gaps are filled in.
(c) New U-shaped ribs (A) are inserted as the weaving begins to need support, giving the basket its shape.

47

spells are secured to a frame of riven ash or hazel which has been steamed and formed into a hoop. The progress of the weave is similar to that of the American willow basket.

Simple hoops, incidentally, for children or cooperage, are of hazel or withy rods cut in the spring, riven with a froe or willow cleave leaving the bark intact, shaved on the riven side with a drawknife to make the bending easier, and then soaked or steamed and formed into circles around pegs and nailed together.

Trugs

Traditional Sussex trugs require more skill in the preparation of the materials. The frame (sweet chestnut or ash) is of two riven wands, steamed and shaped round a former into oblong hoops with rounded corners, each hoop closed with little nails. The hoops are set at right angles to each other, the first forming the rim and the second as handle and girth strap. The body of this light basket is of broad oak or willow strips, fitted to the frame rather like the planks of a boat's hull with a wide central strip carefully soaked or steamed and curved to shape, then fixed by small clenched nails at either end to the rim, with the rest of the splats overlapping each other on either side of it. Two pieces of willow act as feet. The most skilful part of trug-making is splitting out the splats, which are very thin and carefully shaped to taper slightly at either end so that the basket's shape is good. Trugs are popular now for gardens, homes and about the farm as well.

Shaving the boards before steaming.

Completed trugs.

Field baskets

Children can make rough field or hedgerow baskets from cedar bark, stripped from dead trees and boiled for ten or fifteen minutes in a solution of water and wood ashes, then laid out on a board to dry, or they can use meadow grasses simply cut and dried, or even the fresh outer covering of corn cobs, torn into strips and soaked in water, then braided before being woven.

Coracles

A coracle is in effect a very open-weave basket of riven coppice rods or wickerwork covered with cured hide or tarred canvas, making a boat light enough to be carried quite easily on your back but requiring considerable skill to control it on the water with a single paddle as you perch on a plank which serves as a seat and, more essentially, as a brace across the craft to maintain the coracle's shape. The framework might be of riven ash woven with hazel rods or osier withies around the rim. There are local differences in the shape of these one-person boats: some are as round as a bowl, some as oval as a beetle, some are more or less oblong at the rim. But in essence they have changed very little since prehistoric times. The round rods are about ½in in diameter before being cleft in two and shaved down with a drawknife to about ¼in thick then soaked in water for a day and night to make them pliable. They are then interlaced flat on the ground — 19 of them in some patterns, 7ft 6in for longways and 6ft 3in for those that go across them. The free ends are carefully curved into uprights and bound at the rim with thin hazel rods after the seat has been put in place.

With perhaps an even longer history than coracles are boats made from bundled reeds. The type is portrayed in ancient Egyptian art and is still made in much the same way in a few places today. For example, one or two Sardinian fishermen know how to lay bundles of long reeds along the length of the boat, binding them in place to a traditional plan measured in handspans, and forming a flat little vessel with a tall prow. The body is stiffened with spars pushed through horizontally and the craft can last for months, though the building takes only a few hours. The technique is the basis of bind-and-coil basketry.

Cane

Cane is the stems of plants like certain small palms (such as rattan and calamus) or large grasses (including split bamboo). In essence cane is round, long and very slender with a woody texture and, like osier, canes are usually soaked before being woven and they set firm when dry. Basketry cane is usually rattan, which is split by means of a plane-like engine: the flat, shiny outside lengths are used for chair seats and the central core for baskets. Indonesia is the world's major cane supplier.

Cane seating

The pleasure in the craft of cane seating is the creation of a pattern from the almost monotonous repetition of the work to build up the familiar octagonal weave. Although it falls outside the 'grow your own and convert it' principles of this book in that you will have to use imported materials, it is so suitable as a cottage industry that it merits inclusion, especially if you combine it with a rush-seating enterprise.

You need the shiny, flat, outer part of split cane for the work. In fact there are basically two types of suitable cane — flat seating cane for the weaving and circular centre cane for pegging at the edges. The cane is graded by number: no. 1 is the finest, 2 and 3 are the most common, 4 is heavier and 6 is used for beading. It is supplied in quarter-kilo hanks and is worked dry or after wrapping in a damp cloth for about half an hour. The aim is to weave so that the shiny side is always uppermost on the seat, without twisting the cane in the chairframe holes or on the underside.

There are two basic patterns (and all sorts of variations on the main themes): single-setting and double-setting. The latter is more commonly seen and is preferable in that it produces a stronger and more durable, rigid weave, and the main difference between the two methods is that the first two 'runs' for double-setting are made with paired canes rather than single ones. The first step is to drill vertical holes for the canes through the frame — perhaps 15–18 on each rail of a chair.

Double-setting

The first settings run between the front and back of the seat frame. Start at the centre hole in the back rail and insert the first cane down through it, holding it in place with a peg. Take the free end over to the front rail (with the shiny side up) and pass it down through the opposite hole; peg it there, come up again through the neighbouring hole to the left (without twisting it) and run it across to the opposite hole on the back rail, and so on towards the lefthand rail. Start the second cane of the pair from the centre hole of the *front* rail, so that you are using the same holes and in parallel with the first cane but in the opposite direction. Leave the centre-hole pegs in place but

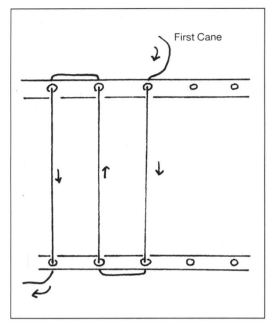

The first cane of the first setting: start at the centre hole in the back rail, entering from below.

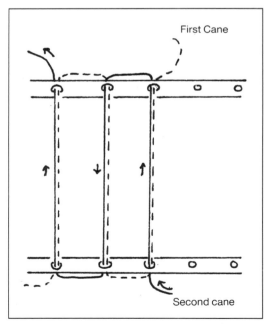

The second cane of the first setting: start at the centre hole in the *front* rail, entering from below, and use the same holes as the first cane but run the second in the opposite direction.

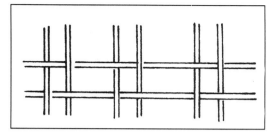

The second settings interwoven with the first settings.

move the others as you proceed. Keep the work firm but not tight and join in new canes as necessary by bringing the end of the old cane up through its hole, inserting the end of the new one down the same hole and knotting it to the old cane where it loops between the holes on the underside, pulling the knot into the hole.

Continue these parallel front/back runs until you reach the lefthand rail, then start new canes from the centre for the right half. Now you are ready for the second settings, which run at right angles across the first settings and are woven among them: start at the front hole on the lefthand rail for the first cane, and at the front hole on the righthand rail for the parallel second cane, and work them as you did the first setting but weave them alternately so that the first cane goes under the lefthand cane of each first-setting pair and over the second of the pair but the second cane goes over the first of the pair and under the second.

The next stage is the diagonals, known as the crossings, and these are worked as single canes rather than in pairs. Start the first crossings at the front lefthand corner hole and weave the cane diagonally over the first pair of settings, under the second pair and so on towards the back righthand corner. The second crossings will start at the front righthand corner and the cane passes *under* the first pair of the first settings, over the first pair of the second settings, and so on.

The finishing touches involve pegging alternate holes and adding beading cane all round the edges, kept in place with loops of couching cane coming up through the hole from below, over the beading and back down through the same hole.

Once you have the knack, you can experiment with fancy frame shapes and fancy patterns in the weave. Cane and wickerwork can be used to make whole chairs, sofas, tables and other furniture: the possibilities are considerable and can be extended beyond furniture to coachwork and — well, you think of something new, perhaps incorporating your bentwood techniques. Bentwood chairs, for example, look delightul with cane seats rather than the perforated plywood they so often sport, and they could be made 'different' if the wood was painted or stained in interesting colours, or if the canework incorporated a special pattern or — and here's a shock for purists — the cane itself could be coloured, or perhaps in more than one colour so that the actual colour forms part of the pattern. Difficult, but a challenge?

Rushes

Rushes, in contrast with reeds, have cylindrical stems with pithy centres: you can idly peel away the greenery and be left with a white column of light cellular material not unlike insulation foam. The old rushlights that were essential to every country cottage made use of the pith's spongelike ability to absorb grease: rushes were cut while still green but fully grown and were trimmed to about 18in in length, then all the green casing was removed except for a full-length strip to support the core of pith. The prepared rushes were laid in melted tallow or wax to soak up the grease and could then be burned to give a rather weak but cheap light. 'Keck' lights are different: they are made from the hollow stems of umbelliferous plants like cow parsley, stuffed with wax-soaked flax. (Those hollow tubes have many other childish uses as whistles, straws, pea-shooters . . .)

If you are very careful, you can make pith ornaments by peeling off all the green from the rushes and then gently plaiting or weaving the piths into whatever shapes you fancy. Unstripped rushes are much tougher: they can easily be twisted, knotted or plaited without breaking and country children know instinctively how to make mats from plaited rushes without anybody showing them the techniques.

For basketry and seating, use the English bulrush *Scirpus lacustris*, which grows in freshwater, or use some of the imported rushes. Traditionally, rush is harvested after midsummer day on a two-year cycle by those who have the precious right to do so and who enjoy being waistdeep in river water. The rushes are then washed and air-dried in partial shade for several days or weeks to 'cure' so that they will not shrink later on. Thereafter they need to be stored in a dry, airy place until required for use. For most purposes, they are dampened before being worked: sprinkle them with water and leave them wrapped up overnight.

Rushes are sold in bolts or bundles 40in in circumference at the butt end, or by weight. In times gone by they were widely used for all manner of applications: apparently, rush baskets made by the ancient Britons were of such high quality that the Romans snapped them up and took them home. For many centuries rushes were simply strewn on the floors of cottage and castle alike, or were made into floor mats, or used for thatching ricks.

Plaiting

Rushes are quite slender but a thicker plait is easily made by using two or three as if they were one in a straightforward three-ply plait (like braiding hair). For a wider plait, use five, seven, nine or even eleven 'plies' or strands: you'll soon work out the basic pattern of the weave as long as you ensure that, wherever it starts, each strand reaches opposite outside edges at regular intervals. Start with the butts of the rushes and discard the brittle pointed tips.

To join in a new strand, make a point of using strands of different lengths so that the joins are always staggered. Simply twist in the new strand's butt during the plaiting, with perhaps a six-inch overlap.

Plaited mats are made by coiling the plaited lengths in a flat plane according to the shape you want and securing with discreet stitches. For a circular mat, work in

snailshell or Swiss roll style. The diagrams show the starting point for ovals, rectangles and squares.

These basic shapes can be used for table mats, or several can be sewn together as floor mats. Plaited ropes can be more ambitiously coiled to make rush baskets (skips), linen baskets, trucklebed mattresses, hats, 'wittle' bags (victual or food pouches for the field), beehives and even furniture such as the draughtproof 'beehive chair'. In fact, if you can do it with straw you can probably do it with rushes, and vice versa.

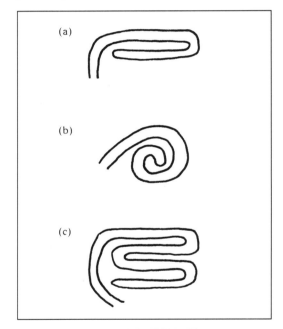

COILED RUSH MATS

(a) Core for an oval mat.
(b) Core for a round mat.
(c) Core for an oblong mat.

Weaving

Finger-flattened rushes can be used without being plaited: they can simply be woven into mats, with round rushes for trimming and finishing. Woven work can be shaped as you go by using basket-weaving techniques and working over a former — perhaps a flower-pot for a basket shape. Formers can also be used to mould shaped articles from plaited lengths.

Rush seating

The techniques for rush seating can also be used with raffia (not nearly as strong), cord, marram grasses and similar materials. They are appropriate to fairly rustic furniture — solid, plain kitchen chairs and stools, for example.

As with all weaving and basketry, there is something very satisfying at the way the pattern builds up from the repetition of simple steps — and how human it is to seek patterns in life and to appreciate the way they develop almost magically of their own accord.

Start with a simple square stool with a frame of *rounded* bars to prevent the material being frayed against sharp edges in use. Dampen and mellow the rushes, then flatten them between finger and thumb, flicking off any brittle tips. The strands will be of two rushes twisted evenly together, butt to tip so that the combined thickness is even, to form a coil much stronger than a plain length (the principle of rope-making) and comfier to sit on than plaited work. New lengths will be tied into the old with reef knots on the underside of the seat.

Tie the ends of two rushes firmly together with string, then tie the string to the middle of the lefthand rail of the stool. Twisting the rushes together as a coil with your right hand as you work, run them parallel to that lefthand rail and then over and under the front rail at the corner. Take the coil over itself and then over and under the lefthand rail at that corner. Now pass it to the right, running parallel to the front rail, and take it over and under the righthand rail at the corner, then over itself and over and under the front rail at the same corner. Next, repeat the process over and under the back rail at its corner with the righthand rail, then over itself and over and under the righthand rail at that corner, and finally over and under the lefthand rail at its corner with the back rail.

That is the basis of the pattern. Continue in an anticlockwise direction by taking the coil over and under the front rail and repeat all the subsequent stages, feeding in new rushes as needed and keeping each new circuit close to the preceding one as you

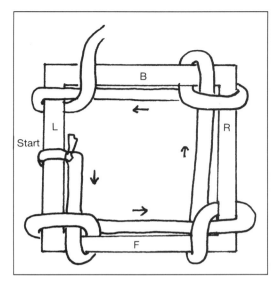

Start by tying the first rush to the middle of the lefthand rail (L). Take it over and round the front rail (F), then over and round (L), then the righthand rail (R), and again (F), then the back rail (B), then (R), (L) and (B), and then back to (F) again to complete the first circuit. Continue in this anticlockwise pattern, working gradually towards the centre of the seat.

work towards the centre. After perhaps ten circuits, pause to pad the seat by firmly stuffing clean materials such as broken rushes or straw between the upper and lower layers of the weave, working from underneath, and then continue.

Natural rush is an attractive material but, you could experiment with dyeing to produce a coloured seat or even a multi-coloured one with contrasting shades incorporated into the four triangles of the woven pattern. Polycord can be bought in a wide choice of colours but rush cord and seagrass tend to be offered in their natural tones.

Straw

Straw is the stems of grain-bearing plants: it is soft and easy to work, often readily available or easy to grow, and it has excellent insulation properties, providing warmth in wall panels and weather protection in thick thatch. It can also be fashioned into all sorts of useful or decorative articles.

Bind-and-coil

Over the centuries, bee-skeps have often been made in the style of human dwellings of the period. At first they were inverted willow baskets (rather like old calf-muzzles) weatherproofed with wool and moss packed under clay daub, just like primitive houses, but for a long time they were of coiled and thatched straw or reed, sometimes set in the sheltering niche of a stone bee-bole. These 'lipwork' or leapwork straw beehives have a very long history and are one of the earliest practical applications of bind-and-coil techniques for baskets. 'Leap' is an Old English word for a basket or a wicker net.

Bundled lengths of straw are simply bound together in ropes and then coiled to form a cylinder in a style not unlike that of coiled pot-making, except that the straw coil can form a continuous spiral. The vessel's shape is maintained by stitching the coils together, traditionally with lengths of briar or bramble cut from the hedgerows in winter, stripped of their thorns and split into four thongs, the pith being discarded. For a beehive, add a lid of coiled straw rope, or perhaps a thatched top, and cut a small entrance hole at the base of the hive.

This simple bind-and-coil technique has many applications, whether in straw (traditionally rye), hay, rushes, reeds or any similar material. You can make platters, trays, tubs, hassocks, chairs, hats, thick soft baskets and many more essentially circular items. The consistency of the circle is maintained by using a measuring ring — commonly a section of cow-horn — through which the ropes of straw are pushed as coiling progresses.

Circularity is not essential, of course. For example, the medieval shepherd's truckle-bed was made in the form of an oblong mat of coiled straw rope pinned together with sharp, light sticks (spicks) pushed in from the sides. It was finished with an upturned lip around the edges to keep out draughts and to keep the bed covering in place. The truckle was quick to make, warm to sleep in and much more comfortable than turf. Straw mattresses under feather beds were common in most homes at the time.

A more elaborate use of the technique, but equally popular in draughty cottages, is in making a hooded beehive chair — lovely to curl up in — and indeed the style found its way into London clubs, where the straw was covered with leather to disguise its humble origins, or with loose chintz in the home. Modern versions, sometimes in cane basketweave, are sometimes suspended so that they swing and sway.

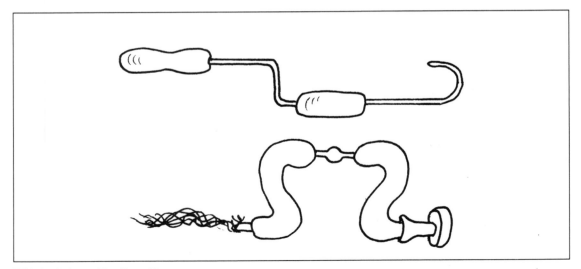

Whimbrels for making Straw Ropes.

Straw rope

A straw rope for use as such (rather than for coiling in lipwork) was often made on the farm, perhaps for tying down a stack or haltering an animal. Two people are needed: a maker and a spinner. The equipment is simply a throwcock or spindle like a carpenter's brace and the work is most comfortably done in a barn, where there is adequate space. The maker sits with a pile of straw (winter wheat for strength, barley for softness) already drawn out into swathes with all the straws lying in the same direction. The rope is started with a hand-twisted loop attached to the spindle, which is held by the spinner, who walks slowly and evenly backwards, away from the maker, winding the spindle to coil the rope together while the maker feeds in new straws. The straw needs to be slightly damp (sprinkle it the night before) and the completed rope is fastened between poles to dry so that it will not untwist when it is released. The technique is the basis for making hemp ropes as well.

Straw hats

Susanna Wood has a highly successful cottage industry based in a converted Oxfordshire farmyard at South Moreton, near Didcot, where her team turn out gloriously colourful hats of straw and raffia decorated with ribbons, velvet, flowers and straw ornaments.

The making of straw hats and bonnets used to be a considerable cottage industry, especially early in the 18th century, until superior Italian imports from Leghorn took over in the 19th century. William Cobbett, in *Cottage Economy* (1823), described the converting of English straw plait into bonnets as 'an advantageous kind of labour' enabling the labourer's family to be constantly employed in cutting, bleaching, sorting and plaiting the straw. Cobbett pointed out that, before the Italian invasion, English 'platt' was made of the straw of ripened grain, whereas the stronger and more beautiful Italian hats were of straw or grass cut green. Ripe straw is already dead while standing and to use it is like making a walking cane from a dead stick: it is bound to break. The

Italians also plaited straw in the round (English straw was split) which gave the hats a much more lively appearance in the contrasting facets of light and shade. And the green Italian straw was bleached by scalding so that it held its colour, in contrast to the English method of bleaching with brimstone which inevitably led to changes in colour later when the hat was exposed to sun and rain.

Cobbett was tireless in his researches to improve the quality of the English cottager's straw plait. He experimented with different species of meadow grass, different times of harvesting wheat straw, different methods of bleaching and different ways of turning the plaits into hats (English plaits were 'put together as boards are put on the side of a barn', overlapping each other, but Leghorn bonnets dispensed with overlapping and the plaits were 'knitted', or simply joined edge to edge with almost invisible seams).

Full details of Cobbett's experiments are given in *Cottage Economy* but his efforts were doomed. In 1870 cheap straw plait came in from China, and the increasing use of machine-sewn plaits had already brought a considerable decline to cottage straw-workers, even in their strongholds in Essex, Bedfordshire, Hertfordshire and Buckinghamshire. Then in the 1890s Japanese imports led to the total collapse of the home industry.

Here is the traditional method of making English straw hats. First, bleach the straw (probably with hydrogen peroxide today — Cobbett's method is complicated and laborious) or dye it if you are using colours. Split straw can be produced with a knife or with the aid of a splitting engine, which is a set of sharp blades (steel or bone) surrounding a sharp prong. Push the engine into the straw and press between finger and thumb to split it away in ribbons. Flatten the split straw with a rolling pin or a splint mill, which has two boxwood rollers turned by a handle.

Moisten the straw (traditionally by drawing it across your tongue) and plait it. There are numerous local patterns, some using whole rather than split straw — for example a four-straw plait for a field basket with handles and flap-lid. Other plaits include Double Whipcord (using seven straws, double), Satin (nine straws), Short Cake (eleven), Diamond (thirteen) and Brilliant (two dozen straws and so many facets that it seems to sparkle).

Wind the plait into hats, sewing it into place as you proceed and modelling the shape on a woodblock former, or machine-block it using heat and moisture. You can use a treadle sewing machine or invest in an electric one.

How about becoming a horse milliner? It used to be a craft, making sunhats for horses complete with ear-pieces and fringes to ward off the flies. With the likely changes in climate from the greenhouse effect now more of a reality than a vague possibility, perhaps there is scope for kitting out the increasing number of leisure horses in Britain. Visions of bonneted Shetlands, or polo ponies going cross-eyed under dangling corks, or the Derby winner wearing a boater with straw blinkers attached . . .

Or how about coats for cows? The Japanese are now providing their cows with straw jackets to protect their heads, backs and bellies from the sun — and sunglasses as well. It might sound a little ridiculous to you but in fact it is all too true that cattle are far more likely to suffer in hot weather than in cold, and a sunbaked cow spends so much time seeking relief from the heat that she has a greatly reduced appetite and therefore greatly reduced milk yields. The sunglasses have the added bonus of protecting the eyes from insects and from the skin cancers which so often affect the eyes of certain European cattle breeds in tropical climates.

Straw ornaments

Straw is such a versatile material and when it is readily to hand many an idle set of fingers has twisted it nonchalantly into shapes, making little knotted ornaments or braided columns and loops or corn dollies or harvest festival decorations or button-hole ornaments and favours or gold-and-silver Christmas ornaments. Some of these are created by plaiting around a central core of

Straw ornaments.

straws and the pattern of the plait forms itself into a spiralling column, or a straight tubular column formed round a temporary stick (do you remember those children's French knitting dollies, four pins and a hollow wooden core?).

Follow Cobbett's advice to use the section of straw from the upper joint of the stem to the head (the grain heads are sometimes left on as ornamentation). Use it freshly cut, or dampen it if it has become stiff.

Straw can also be used to make picture frames or in the form of marquetry: paste coloured straws in patterns to cover mats and boxes.

Straw briquettes

In theory, turning straw into convenient, compact little logs for domestic open fires and stoves is a good commercial outlet for those with surplus straw or those with enough capital to invest in a briquetting machine and become travelling contractors. The problem, apart from the very high cost of the machine, is in marketing the product, and that is a pity. When briquettes were first made on more than a 'take a handful of straw and some coal dust and paste' basis, I bought them by the bagful from a local farm and was delighted with the results on an old Rayburn and as starter fuel for a wood fire. Their calorific value can be quite a lot higher than that of unseasoned wood and compares reasonably with ordinary domestic coal, especially if retail prices are taken into account.

In essence, baled straw is smashed to pieces to break down its ligna cellulose and then the particles are compressed in a die to form logs. Before the machinery was invented, a few hardy souls really did handmake briquettes with a mixture of coaldust, sawdust, straw and a little cement and water to make a dough which was pressed into wooden moulds or through a length of pipe. One wonders if it was worth the effort.

Thatching

Like so many country crafts, thatching is an art which relies more on experience and intuition than textbooks and measurements. People have thatched their dwellings with plant material since they first began to make their own shelters, in all parts of the world. In this country, thatching materials include straw, reed, heather (ling) and bracken — the last two have longer histories but straw and reed are now by far the most common. Water reed thatch has a life of perhaps fifty or sixty years, combed wheat reed twenty-five to forty, and long-straw thatch only ten to twenty.

Reed

Thatching reed might literally be water reed, especially Norfolk reed, but the term is also applied to combed wheat straw, known as Devon reed, which is laid to give the dense, brushlike finish of a water reed thatch in contrast to the softer look of long-straw thatch.

Water reed (*Phragmites*) is by far the strongest and longest lasting of the thatching materials; indeed, it was often incorporated as bedding in plaster walls where, with its relatively high silica content (durable in itself) further preserved by the plaster's lime, it could last for centuries. It grows in fresh or salt water in lowland and coastal marshes or ditches and ponds but it needs to be properly managed. The reed beds should be kept flooded for most of the year, and the water should be moving rather than stagnant. Weeds need careful controlling (by flooding or burning) to extend the life of the beds. If you are growing your own reeds for thatching, you will probably try to harvest them annually (commercial growers tend to harvest for heavier crops every two years) and, with skill, you might make about 400 bundles per acre. You can scythe them by hand or mechanically with something like an old Allen scythe: harvest from mid December onwards, after the leaf has fallen and the flag is down, but stop harvesting before you damage the young 'colts', which appear in late April. Top quality reeds have a stem diameter of 2–6 mm (ideally 3–4 mm at the cut base) and a length of 90–180 cm (best at 137–153 cm). Bundles are about 55 cm in circumference measured at 30 cm above the base cut and 15–20 cm just below the flowerheads. Six bundles make a fathom.

Straw

Thatching straw is a crop grown deliberately for the purpose, with grain as its byproduct. A thatcher requires long, straight, thin, bright and moderately stiff straw with hollow stems. Most thatchers use wheat straw, though traditionally rye was always popular. Oat and barley straw might be suitable for temporary cover if densely packed: oat straw is not really tough enough and barley straw, which is soft, finds better uses on a livestock farm. Winter wheat is greatly superior to spring-sown wheat.

The straw grower's first problem is to choose a suitable variety — not short-strawed but not so long that it falls flat on its face as it grows. The popular old varieties included Elite, Little Joss and Square-headed Masters but you could experiment with Maris Widgeon or Maris Huntsman. (Grain yields are higher in these newer varieties, if that is what you want, but straw yields are higher in the older types.) The crop needs far less nitrogen than a commercial farmer would deem necessary for a cereal crop and it should be harvested when the grain is still slightly cheesy, the straw slightly green at the nodes. It must on no account be cut with a combine harvester, which would ruin the straw, nor should it be baled. Use an old-fashioned binder, which will be much more gentle. Let the sheaves dry where they lie for a day or two before stacking them in an airy barn or under thatch or canvas outside; or stook the bound sheaves in the field for up to two weeks to ripen before storing. Take every precaution to avoid fungal attack. The straw should be presented bright, clean and dry to the thatcher and should be from the current harvest.

For *long-straw* work, the crop can go through a drum thresher and perhaps be bunched in a straw trusser (if you can find one). The thresher will probably break many of the stems and mix up rubbish such as crop leaves with the straw. Long-straw thatch, which has plenty of stem-length exposed to the elements, is typical of south east, southern and central England; else-where combed wheat reed or Norfolk reed are preferred.

For Devon reed or *combed straw*, the crop used to be put into a reed-press consisting of two pieces of timber about 10ft long laid on a stool. The sheaf was put in the press: the worker took hold of the ears, drew out the straw by hand (and at that stage it can be called reed), cut off the caps and bound the sheaf ready for use. It could outlast long-straw thatch by ten years or more. Today a special iron-toothed reed-comber mechanically strips off the loose leaves, combs out the general rubbish and extracts the grain but the stalks themselves do not go through the threshing mechanism, so that they are not bruised. The straw emerges as tidy trussed bundles with all the butts at one end.

Thatching terms and tools

Thatching terminology varies regionally, of course, and a word commonly pronounced 'elm' or 'ellum' might be written as *yelm*, yealm, yolm, holm or helem. It describes a small bundle of thatching straw. Each yelm is in fact several smaller yelms firmly bound together with binder twine or a twist of straw. With long straw, a heap of straw is sprinkled with water (it needs to be slightly damp) and then handfuls are straightened against the thatcher's leg with swift, gentle hand strokes so that a random handful becomes a tidy sheaf, about 6–8in in diameter, with all the straws parallel to each other and all the short straws and weeds combed out by hand. The small yelms are bundled together, butts and heads alternately and each set slightly slanted against its neighbours so that the small yelms can readily be separated from the bundle later when the binding is cut. Traditionally, the yelms for rick thatching were prepared on the farm in this way in spring and summer, ready for covering the rick after the harvest; the bundles were in the meantime stacked tidily in rows, side by side with ends touching, and temporarily roofed with sloping yelms to shed rainwater.

Bundles of yelms can be carried aloft in a *hod* — a catapult-shaped branch about 5ft long with a peg and rope at the top of one arm to keep it in place on the roof. The hod might also be called hoc, yoke, yack, jack, fork, bow and so on.

Thatching *spars* (or spicks, specs, spears, springles, pegs, pins, botches, broaches etc.) are wooden pegs for fastening the new thatch to the old. They vary in length from about 18in to 4ft, depending on the job. They are made from willow or hazel rods about 2in thick, cleft while green exactly through the middle so that half the brown core is in each piece; then they are cleft again, making at least four spars (experts can split out more from a rod). The blade of the small spar hook is very sharp and is worked towards your hand: take care!

Spars are pointed at both ends by means of three deft strokes with the spar hook. Then they are bundled and bound with willow withies, hazel bonds or strong string at top and bottom. Each spar is white on two sides and barked on its back. For use, they are bent into a hairpin shape, either at the time of splitting (if the spar-maker is also thatcher) or during the work after being soaked to restore pliability. They are bent with a quick twist of the wrists, so that the fibres do not break. In use, they are thrust down into the thatch and driven sharply home with a gloved hand or wooden mallet.

An essential tool is a thatching *rake* to comb down the straw during the work. Make your own by studding an old handle with nails or use an old hay-rake head. Equally important is a strong leather *palm pad* to protect your hand when driving spars or sweeping the straw: you will maintain a better work flow by using your hands rather than switching to different tools. You also need leather *knee pads* as you will spend much of your time kneeling against the ladder rungs.

The *ladder* needs to be quite long and with rounded uprights so that it can easily be rolled over across the roof to a new position rather than slid or jerked across.

Cutting equipment includes a thatcher's knife to cut the block patterns in double thatch over a house's ridge or for cutting flattened borders at the eaves before finishing off neatly with pointed shears (which are like sheep-shears except that they are cranked out of alignment to avoid knuckle-rasping). The thatcher's knife chops downwards; if you need to cut on a horizontal plane use a thatcher's eaves knife with a sawing motion: it has a long, curved blade on a short handle.

Basic thatching

As a learner, begin by practising on a rick rather than a house until you have understood the principles. You would be well advised to learn from an experienced thatcher or to attend at least a basic course first. A six-month crash course with the Thatching Advisory Service at Finchampstead would cost you several thousand pounds but you will be given a local franchise and continuing support.

The steeper the pitch of the roof, the more readily rainwater will be shed before it can soak into the straw and rot it: if you are designing a new roof, pitch it at perhaps 40–50 degrees. Very broadly, you start at the eaves and work upwards to the ridge. Long-straw thatch is laid in strips a foot or two wide: each strip, or *steltch*, is completed from eaves to ridge before the neighbouring strip is laid. With reed, on the other hand, work from left to right across the roof in courses.

The eaves layers are important and should be designed to throw off roof water well clear of the building: the lowest layer must therefore project for a good distance. With long straw, the first layer is doubled over with butts down to form 'bottles' or 'dollies' at the eaves; the second layer in the steltch is also butts down and completely overlaps the first but all subsequent layers are tops down and cover only about two-thirds of the previous layer, continuing thus all the way to the ridge before starting a second steltch from the eaves and tucking it closely against the first. For combed reed thatch, use a *leggett* (a grooved wooden bat) to dress the courses so that only a couple of inches of the butts are visible on the surface of the thatch. You need a metal-faced legget for water reed.

Each layer can either be pinned to underlying thatch with spars or, in a stripped or new roof, tied to the rafters with twine. Long hazel rods (*liggers* or ledgers) can be run horizontally over the thatch for the full length of the roof near ridge and eaves, pegged down with spars, to give extra security and a good look: you could alternatively use straw-rope, also pinned by hairpin-twisted spars, or strong twine simply double-looped and tied around straight spars used like stakes. There are several other methods of securing the yelms using iron crooks driven into the rafters, for example, or literally stitching them down with the aid of an outsized steel needle and the help of an assistant underneath.

At the ridge, the yelms from either side of the roof must knit together even if it is only a rick. For house thatch, decoration is almost as important as function: take the yelms to the ridge line then lay a thick final row, bending it over the top and holding it on either side with a pattern of hazel liggers and cross rods. There are many individual ways of dealing with the ridge and most involve inserting rolls of straw along the line of the ridge under the wrapover yelms, and adding decorative touches by block-cutting scallops and other patterns in the thatch.

Ine and Eric Puffet, a prolific thatching team based at Kings Nympton near Umberleigh in North Devon, top all their work with a straw owl — partly as a trademark but also to deter birds thinking of nesting in the thatch. Most thatchers have a straw trademark, perhaps a bird or small mammal.

Finally, as a more direct bird and rodent deterrent, cover the whole of the thatch with wire netting after the eaves have been trimmed tidily.

For heather thatch, use longish shoots of ling (*Calluna vulgaris*) which have grown more or less prostrate. Cut them in late autumn or winter and lay them in swathes tied in place with twine and further secured with pegs, fingercombing as you work. Lay the ling as you would reed.

3 Meadow, Hedgerow and Garden

This chapter considers some of the plant and animal produce which can be raised on the holding or harvested from the wild and then converted into food, drinks, decorations, cosmetics, remedies and household aids. The actual processes of brewing, preserving, drying, distilling and so on are described in the appropriate sections (The Stillroom, The Brewhouse, Kitchencraft, The Dairy). Note that plants such as hemp and flax are considered separately in the Fibre chapter along with wool and hair.

Wild harvest

Think of hedgerows and no doubt you have instant memories of childhood blackberrying, your lips and fingers stained purple and the smell of berries warmed by the sun. Isn't it odd that brambles are so often considered a nuisance in the garden, to be ruthlessly removed, yet in someone else's hedge or along a woodland ride they are the source of so much delight? Their produce is more than berries for pies, jellies and wine, in fact. The canes, stripped of thorns, have always been used by country dwellers as binders (in basketry, for example) and their leaves as tonics for livestock. The flowers are pretty, too.

Many other common hedgerow plants have parts which can be eaten — fruit, nuts, buds, leaves — or turned into healthy juices or alcoholic drinks, or used in herbal remedies and cosmetics.

Think of meadows and you might think of mushrooms — the magic of hunting for those secret white buttons in the grass after it has been freshened by a September shower. In the woods, of course, there are all sorts of redolent fungi which, to those who have faith in their knowledge, are often quite delicious. If you are really lucky, and have a well trained dog or pig, you might even find some truffles. Above all, meadows produce flowers and herbs galore — and I mean meadows, not monocrop silage fields of Italian ryegrass heavily dressed with nitrogen. It is noticeable that wild flowers seem to prefer much lower nutrient levels than many intensively grown agricultural crops.

For worthwhile cottage industries, it might be best to concentrate on one or two types of conversion — winemaking, perhaps, or preserves or remedies — and combine hedgerow and meadow harvesting with produce grown in your own garden and orchard so that you are more in control of production flows and can be quite sure that the produce is not contaminated by exhaust fumes or drifting agricultural sprays. If you are offering organic products, can you be sure that your wild harvest really is all you would wish it to be?

There is something very agreeable about the idea of country wines, herbal cures and tonics, 'green' domestic cleaning recipes, handcrafted decorative items from flowers and seeds, or perhaps a wild-harvest restaurant, catering service and mail-order business offering preserves, wines, home-baked pies, wildfruit ice-creams — even better if you can also provide organic dairy produce and honey from your own or a friend's holding, and perhaps homegrown meat as well. A menu might include wild rabbit with herbs (wild rabbit, kindly and cleanly killed without being filled with shotgun pellets, is one of the healthiest meats there is in our cholesterol-conscious times), freshwater fish, a variety of edible fungi, elderflower fritters, mead, hedge and meadow salads (nutty young hawthorn leaves, dandelion leaves, chicory, herbs, wild garlic and plenty more), hazelnut dishes, rosehip syrup — the possibilities are unlimited.

There might also be an excellent cottage venture in collecting wild seed to grow new hedging plants, by the thousand, or to help preserve wild tree species which are becoming less common (such as the wild service tree) or to grow pretty shrubs like spindle and guelder rose for the garden, or large numbers of native hardwood saplings for conservation projects, or plants for butterfly reserves. Perhaps you could make a life's work of breeding new garden varieties from wild species or specialise in scented wildflowers like honeysuckle and that lovely garden escapee, Dame's Violet (Sweet Rocket), which seeds so readily, grows two or three feet tall and smells like the most cosseted garden stocks. Take care in the case of wildflowers: many are protected species and you should certainly avoid digging them up or vandalising them in any way, which includes picking bunches of them.

Many decorative items can be made from your wild harvest — autumn-leaf lampshades, dried grasses for flower arrangements and pictures, pressed flowers to decorate mirrors and picture frames, for example.

Cultivated plants

Fruit

Be imaginative in your orchard: grow some of the older and now rare varieties of apples and pears, or specialise in cider and perry types. Try interesting fruits such as medlars, quinces, mulberries, blueberries, wine-berries, figs. Fruit can be sold freshly harvested, or preserved by bottling, in jams and jellies and cheeses, or pressed for juice, or fermented, or chopped into your dairy's yogurts . . .

Flowers and vegetables

Although you might make a small income from growing and selling fresh cottage vegetables, cut flowers and bedding or pot plants grown in the garden, profitable cottage industries are based on plants which large-scale growers cannot or will not bother to grow. For example, you might try early lily-of-the-valley (my grandmother used to grow them in quantity and was up before dawn to pick them and take them to a local flower market or, sometimes, all the way into the city) or unusual vegetables, or foliage for florists. Even better, grow plants for converting in some way, such as dried flowers or distilled aromatics.

To dry flowers you can simply hang them in bunches, heads downwards, in a dry, airy place out of the sun. For better retention of colour, they should be powder-dried in fine, dry sand from a builder's merchant or in powdered borax: either lay the flower stems horizontally in a box of the powder, or suspend them head down in a tall container, with the heads close to each other but not actually touching, and carefully add sand, without distorting the stems, to surround the flowers completely. Daffodils can be dried in silica gel but will need varnishing afterwards to protect them from atmospheric moisture. Daffodils? Why not? Experiment — you do not need to restrict your flower-drying to the standard everlastings.

To dry lavender, pick the stems just as the flowers begin to lose colour. Choose a dry day and cut when the bushes are not in direct sunlight, but make sure the spikes are dry. Hold the stem ends briefly over a candle flame to seal them, then spread them on brown paper in a single layer in a cool, airy, shady place to dry slowly. Turn the spikes over every few days for two or three weeks until the sap has gone and the petals fall off. Petals dried in this way should retain their qualities for at least three years.

Herbs

Lavender is usually classed as a herb rather than a dried flower (it is used in distilling and cooking, for example). Every cottage garden has room for a good range of herbs for use in the home and they are an obvious choice for a cottage industry if you have the dedication to specialise in their growth, harvesting, conversion and marketing.

Herbs can be sold freshly picked, frozen or dried, or growing in attractive pots (especially earthenware ones, with etched earthenware labels rather than plastic tags). Alternatively, give your crop 'added value' — a term which implies that the raw material is processed in some way before it is sold. If you grow your own produce (herbs or anything else) and convert it yourself, naturally your profit margins should be better but your life will be more complicated. 'Added value' is the essence of this book.

Harvesting herbs

Collect herbs after the dew has disappeared and they have warmed a little so that their essential oils have been drawn up into the leaves but before the heat of the day causes the oils to evaporate (one of the functions of the oils is to cool the plant by evaporation). Harvest just before flowering time for maximum flavour and tenderness in the leaves. If you are interested in the flowers, collect them on a dry day at about midday just as they become fully open. Gather seeds when they are fully ripe, catching them before they are shed, and on a warm day. Roots and bark also play a role in herbal remedies: dig up roots when the plant's top growth is beginning to die back in the autumn, and peel bark when the weather is damp.

Chilling

Herbs will keep fresh in a refrigerator for a few days if they are in a plastic bag, full of air and tightly secured. Deep freezing retains flavour and colour and also most of the plant's nutritional value: put the material in plastic bags and freeze it whole, or chop it up in water and freeze in ice-cube trays.

Drying

Gather the herbs on a dry day for good colour. Clean them well but do not wash them and do not dry them in the sun — the oils will evaporate. Dry the herbs immediately after harvesting, and dry them as quickly as possible but preferably by a gradual withdrawal of moisture rather than risking the loss of the essential oils by oven-drying. Some people dry culinary herbs quickly in a microwave oven, which preserves flavour but might destroy some of the qualities of medicinal herbs. Try drying leaves in a dark, warm, but well ventilated place, like a large airing cupboard, ideally at about 32°C (90°F) for the first day and night and then at 75–80°F for perhaps four days. Have the herbs hanging upside down in bunches or spread them on brown paper over a grid of some kind to help the air to circulate. Dry them to the texture of fragile paper but not so much that they crumble into a powder.

Dried herbs can be put into bags or airtight dark-glass bottles and stored in a dry place protected from sunlight. Watch out for any hint of moisture, which will quickly result in mould and deterioration.

TABLE 3

Herb Thoughts

Culinary flowers	Remedies	Candle scents	Flies: mint, cloves,
Herb oils	Dyes	Laundry rinses	citrus peel
Herb vinegars	Papers	Hair rinses	Nettle tea: lotion to
Floral vinegars	Inks	Antiseptics	soothe minor
Herbal teas, syrups	Cosmetics	Toys, trinkets	insect stings,
Herb-stem baskets	Aromatics		and nettle stings
for potpourri,	Aromatherapy	PEST	
dried flowers	Herb pillows	REPELLENTS	CLEANERS
Potpourri,	Clothes fresheners	Ants: chilli powder,	Rhubarb leaves
pomanders	Drawer sachets	mint	(brass, pans)
Cleaning aids	Bath additives	Insects: vinegar	Ivy (shiny fabric
Pest repellents	Incense	Mice: pepper	restorer)

Spices

It is possible but hardly economical to grow your own exotic spices — for example I recently planted a ginger root which had decided to sprout after it had already been partially grated for kitchen use and, in the record-breaking summer temperatures of 1990, the shoots grew so fast that you could almost see them moving. (I have some experimental sweet potatoes turning into greenhouse bushes as well but they are still several months away from cropping!)

However, there is a much less exotic but very popular 'spice' which grows naturally in Britain and that is mustard. Even in 1823 William Cobbett was protesting that bought mustard was half drugs and flour and was injurious to health: he suggested it was much better to grow your own mustard in the garden. It would be brown rather than yellow, and you would need a mill to grind the seeds, but the flavour was excellent.

Several people do indeed produce and sell mustard, in attractive stoneware or glass jars and very different to dear old Colman's. They might add honey or flavoured vinegars or perhaps whisky, beer and other alcohols to make an unusual product, and some are quite delicious. You could sell your own concoctions with the type of food mustard should accompany — perhaps home-cured ham, smoked meats and farmhouse cheeses.

Tobacco

Herbal tobaccos are usually made from coltsfoot cured with liquorice, sugar, salt and saltpetre and are often mixed with a choice of other herbs like lavender, chamomile, rosemary, thyme, yarrow and so on. Enough to make a nicotine addict weep?

Although the true tobacco plant is a native of America, it can be grown in Britain on a small scale. The secret lies more in the curing, however, than the growing. Harvest the leaves as they ripen, which is a gradual process from the base of the plant upwards over about a month. The leaves change colour slightly and have a tendency to curl as they mature, or become mottled or transparent in texture. Choose a dry day

for harvesting and put the leaves in the sun to wilt for three or four hours, then stack them in small heaps covered with a clean sack to 'sweat' for another four or five days, turning them occasionally, until they are uniformly yellowed.

Now hang them up to dry: slit the midribs about ¾in from the base and thread the leaves on a wire or cane, half an inch apart and face to face, back to back. Small leaves can be threaded on strong twine with a needle. Leave them suspended in a warm but well ventilated shed or attic until the midrib has dried out and is no longer fleshy. The leaves should feel like chamois leather. If they have become too dry and brittle, sprinkle them gently or put them in a damp place until they are pliable.

Remove the midrib and woody laterals with a very sharp blade, then flavour according to taste — perhaps sprinkling the tobacco with diluted treacle, or rum, or prune juice. For a dark brownish-black tobacco, try a solution of stick liquorice dissolved in hot water with enough honey or black treacle to make a thin syrup which can be painted on to each leaf — just a little and not so much that it oozes.

Pack the flavoured leaves in shallow boxes and press them under heavy weights for a fortnight; take them out, cut the wads into thirds, dampen them with the flavouring again, then stack and re-press for at least two or three weeks, or perhaps months. By then you will have a block of cured baccy. Tie it with twine and store it in a dry place for a month or two. Slice and rub it when you want to use it.

Teazels

Teazels used to be grown as a crop, especially in western England, because their thistle-like barbed heads were invaluable for raising the nap on woollen cloth, pulling out all the loose weedseeds and fibres. They grow wild, and splendidly, in my own cottage garden — most stately feature plants taller than a man, their soft purple flowerheads beloved by bees and hoverflies. The soil hereabouts is streamborne sand and silt over heavy yellow clay and the crop does best on stiff, tenacious

Teazels: self-sown and taller than a greenhouse.

Dye plants

There are hundreds of different plants, and different parts of plants, which have traditionally been used as dyes. Appendix I gives just a few of them. Details of mordants to fix dyes and methods of dyeing fibres are given in the Fibre section, but here are a couple of very old dye plants deliberately grown as crops.

Saffron

Saffron was once the product of a major industry in eastern England (hence Saffron Walden). The purple flowers of *Crocus sativus* were intensively grown for their three orange-yellow stigmas, which were dried and used for colouring butter, rice or hair, or flavouring various food dishes, or dyeing fabric a strong yellow, or as a carminative to relieve flatulence, an appetite stimulator (added to herb liqueur), a digestive aid, a remedy against cramp, an emmenagogue to restore or bring on menstruation, and as an aphrodisiac. Someone was doing a good marketing job on the product!

The species is native to Arabia and needs a good hot summer to flower successfully. The site should be sunny and sheltered, and the soil rich and well drained. It is very much a labour-intensive crop: there is no way you could mechanise the harvesting and extraction of the stigmas.

Woad

Isatis tinctoria produces the blue dye we immediately associate with ancient Britons. Traditionally, it was a most tedious plant to convert. Either the leaves were stripped off the standing plant or the whole stem was chopped down in full leaf. The leaves or plants were laid on racks or hurdles in the sun to wither and dry, then they were ground into a paste — by means of pestle and mortar for small quantities, or commercially through rotary wooden rollers at woad mills. Next, the paste was formed into small balls and left to dry under cover for a couple of weeks, then ground up and left to ferment in warm conditions (65–70°F) for several more weeks, after which the mixture

clay or marl. It is a biennial plant, sown broadcast at the end of March and weeded and thinned at the six-leaf stage. After a final thinning the plants should be about 15in apart. Some can be transplanted to another plot in the autumn if you wish: they will come good at the same time as the rest.

Hoe well in autumn and the following March to keep the ground weed-free and encourage the crop's good growth. Severe or late frosts will check the plants, and they can also suffer badly from aphids. They flower during the summer.

When teazels were used by nappers, the dry heads were fixed on a large revolving wheel or teazel frame, like a huge currycomb, which was held by two men as they worked it vertically down against the hanging cloth.

was stirred well, made into round cakes and set to dry again. The dye was made by soaking the cakes in water and fixing it by adding limewater.

Did the ancient Brits really do all that? Try this instead. Chop up and boil fresh leaves for several minutes, strain off and cool the liquor (discarding the leaves) and add a drop or two of liquid ammonia. Whisk busily to aerate the mixture until the froth is pale blue, then warm the liquor to hand-hot and sprinkle it with a little sodium dithionite (without stirring). Be prepared for a shock: it will turn yellow, but don't worry. Leave it to cool to room temperature and then soak your wool in it. Magically, the yarn will turn blue as it dries.

The stillroom

A stillroom is where you distill, or convert a liquid to a vapour by heating it and then condense the vapour back into a concentrated and purer liquid. Essentially it is extraction of the properties you wish to exploit, by means of evaporation and condensation. In practice, a stillroom is a domestic room in which herbs are preserved and converted for medicinal, cosmetic and aromatic uses, whereas a distillery is where you extract spirits in the production of alcohol. The making of alcoholic drinks is covered in the Brewhouse section.

Aromatics

The smell of an aromatic plant is concentrated in its essential oils. These volatile essences, found in flowers, leaves and stems, evaporate when rubbed or heated (for example, by the sun) and release their aroma, which seems to ward off fungal attacks and pests on the one hand and attract beneficial insects on the other, as well as cooling the plant by the process of evaporation.

Quite apart from their value to the plant, the oils are appreciated by humans for fragrances, food flavouring and preservatives. Many seem to have healing properties as an additional bonus and for thousands of years people have practised the art of capturing plant essences for medicinal, cosmetic and culinary use. It is a complex and time-consuming process and, although in theory it would be delightful to convert your own garden flowers and herbs into perfumes and massage oils, it might be impractical to try. For example, you need about a ton of rose petals to produce half a pint of essential oil, or the crop from half an acre of lavender to make one pound of lavender oil.

The oils are extracted by distillation: the plant matter is heated to release its essences in steam, which is then cooled so that it condenses as a purified liquid. The main methods include *enfleurage* for flowers (the petals are spread on a tray and lightly coated with purified fat which picks up their scent so that the essential oil can be extracted by rendering the fat and separating out the oil) or, for foliage and stems, a still with a coil, in which the plant matter is steamed: the vaporised oils mingle with the steam and both are cooled in the coil and collected in a vessel, where the condensed oils separate out from the water. Distillation with steam remains the simplest effective way of extracting the oils from flowers, though some are destroyed by the process; thus essences like lilac and lily-of-the-valley are now extracted with the help of carbon dioxide or by passing petroleum ether through the flowers and distilling to form a wax. Any equipment for extraction is much too expensive and complicated for a cottage industry, however, and it is more practical to buy essential oils from those who specialise in their production on a large scale or from specialist retailers. Choose your source with care: a bandwagon is already rolling.

Essential oils should be treated with great respect: they are often a hundred times as concentrated as they were in the plant and this can make them dangerous to handle. Never use them on the skin without first diluting them. Just a drop of lemongrass oil dabbed on to a woman's clothes as a scent seeped through to her skin and fanned out to give her a large and intensely painful burn, the scars of which were still visible and uncomfortable several months later. In rare cases, the ingestion of essential oils can lead to miscarriage or can be carcinogenic.

For use on the skin, essential oils of any kind should be diluted at the rate of one drop to fifty drops of a carrier oil (such as wheatgerm or sweet almond oil). Those labelled as aromatherapy oils have already been diluted in a carrier oil for massage purposes but note that the 'shelf life' of an essential oil is reduced to a few months as soon as it is mixed with a carrier oil.

Essential oils must be stored in dark-glass containers with airtight seals and kept in a dark, cool environment (but not in a refrigerator), where they will last for a few years if undiluted. The range is considerable: Ivan Day's excellent book *Perfumery with Herbs*, published in association with the Herb Society, gives details of more than 130 essential oils from different parts of the world and he also offers a comprehensive bibliography including books published as long ago as the 16th and 17th centuries with splendid titles like *The Accomplished Lady's Delight*, *Odorographia*, *The Curious Distillatory* and *A Discovery of Infinite Treasure hidden since the World's Beginning*. You can appreciate that the stillroom is able to grip the imagination!

Cosmetics

Those magnificent old books are hard to find but if you are excited by the idea of using herbs and flowers in the stillroom there are some beautiful and detailed modern books such as Leslie Bremness's *The Complete Book of Herbs* published with the National Trust. In that book, and several others, there are informative details about raw materials and their uses, and recipes for household aids, remedies, cooking and cosmetics. Cottage beauty and health products can be appealing both to the producer and the customer: they strike a deep nostalgic chord in most people and evoke a romantic mixture of summer gardens and the rural self-sufficiency of times gone by. Begin by making cosmetics for personal use, experimenting with the wide range and combinations of ingredients which can often be found in the garden and

growing wild — like the invaluable elder, despised as a weed by foresters and hedgers but cherished by every other country dweller in Europe for its almost magical properties, its elusively light bouquet and its berries rich in vitamin C.

If you intend to sell your own cosmetics, you should be aware that different people have different allergies: some will react to certain ingredients and others will not. Users should always test the cosmetic by putting a little on the skin of the inner arm and covering it for twenty-four hours to see if there is an adverse reaction. This is especially important with facial applications.

Here are some basic ideas to give you a grounding in cottage cosmetics. There is great scope for creating your own special products from old recipes or using your imagination combined with modern knowledge to make something highly original.

Waters

Floral waters are not simply flowers and herbs infused in water. You need to fix the aroma of herbal infusions with oil or alcohol (the latter is stronger): make a strong floral infusion, adding 20 per cent by volume of 90 per cent-proof ethyl alcohol or 30 per cent by volume of 60 per cent-proof vodka. For example, you could put a cupful of rose petals or lavender flowers with a quarter-cup of ethyl alcohol at room temperature in a screwtop jar and leave it to infuse for six days, shaking the jar daily. Strain, and store in dark-glass containers. Or you could use essential oils in alcohol.

Creams and lotions

The basic ingredients of skin creams are oil, wax and scented water. Melt the chosen waxes gently, beat in some warmed oils, then slowly trickle warmed water into the mixture and stir until it cools. Add essential oils for their properties and fragrances. Typical ingredients are beeswax, lanolin, almond oil, soy or wheatgerm oils, avocado oils, glycerine and borax with various infusions, floral waters and essential oils.

The greater the proportion of wax, the firmer the cream; more oil makes it softer, and more water makes it lighter. For a spongy texture, add mucilaginous herbs. For a handcream try glycerine, bay rum, ammonia water and rose water; add petroleum jelly for a barrier cream. Store creams and lotions in sealed jars in the fridge and use within a few weeks. Try avocado or ripe peach as moisturisers and try a mixture of beeswax, apricot kernel oil, calendula oil and a few drops of lemon or orange essential oil as a lip salve.

Skin refreshers

Make infusions of, say, elderflower, lavender, orangeflower, rose or sage with witch hazel and a little glycerine — use within three days or buy distilled waters of the flowers, which will last much longer. Astringents include cucumber, strawberry, rosemary, tomatoes or lemon juice. For an aftershave, make up a herbal 'water' but use witch hazel instead of ethyl alcohol.

Face packs and steams

Steam is a great cleanser. For your own use, simply add fresh or dried herbs to boiling water in a bowl and hold your face over the steam with a towel as a hood to retain it (as if you were using Friars Balsam). For face-packs, use liquidised herbs or add fuller's earth or finely ground almond or oatmeal. Add milk to soften and bleach, or honey to heal, or lavender for acne, or eggyolk on a dry skin or eggwhite for an oily one.

Baths

The simplest way of turning a bath into a luxury is to hang herbal tea-bags at the taps for an instant infusion or to add perhaps five drops of essential oils to warm water. You can choose appropriate herbs for relaxation, stimulation or healing, or simply delight in fragrance.

Soap

Soapwort (*Saponaria officinalis*) is quite a pretty herb with pink, scented flowers and is known (and named) for its soapy sap, which is used for laundering, water softening and fabric conditioning. Be warned, however, that it is poisonous if swallowed. Alternatives are soap-bark chips from the South American tree, *Quillaja saponaria* (simmered in hot water) or roots of certain species of Gypsophila.

For 'real' soap you need lye. Collect wood ashes from white woods and put them in a perforated container suspended over a tub. Pour cold water through the ashes so that it trickles slowly into the tub; strain off any particles. This type of lye can be used just as it is to bleach clothes before washing them — simply soak the material in the lye for several days. To make soap, make a strong, thick wood-ash lye (add a little lime to the container) and then add hot grease, at boiling point, and stir the mixture frequently for several days until the soap forms.

An old recipe for soap suggested that lye should be boiled until it was just 'strong enough to eat the feathers off a quill'. In a kettle one-third filled with lye, fill to the top with grease — meat fat, bacon rind, pig skins and what you will — then simmer over a small fire for a few hours. Wash out the grease's dirt by boiling up the soap, once, in a bucket of weak lye and letting the lye and dirt settle to the bottom.

A slightly more complicated method was to melt and clarify salt-free animal fat, strain it through muslin and let it cool in an earthenware basin before mixing in caustic soda (half a pound to 1½ pints of water). The soda causes the mixture to heat up again: set it aside until it is lukewarm. This is the lye. Pour it slowly into lukewarm fat, stir well to cream it together, then pour into moulds and set in a warm place for a day or two. Cut the soap into bars and leave it to harden for a month before use.

Sounds disgusting? Soap boilers were usually banished well away from other people to carry out their admittedly smelly craft! You would do better to buy readymade pure Castile soap and grate it up as the basis for your cottage soaps, melting it and infusing it with the herbs and aromatics of your choice.

Hair treatments

Shampoos can be made from the chopped root or leaves and stems of soapwort infused in boiling water for half an hour with the herbs of your choice. For a dry shampoo, use a mixed powder of orris root and arrowroot, or put floral waters (rose, lavender etc.) on a gauze-covered brush for a between-shampoos hair cleanser.

Hair tonics include nettle, sage, watercress, rosemary, parsley, nasturtium, limetree flowers, calendula, goosegrass, horsetail plants, watercress and many more. For a rinse, infuse herbs in boiling water with lemon juice (fair hair) or vinegar (dark hair).

Make up a hair conditioner based on sunflower or almond oil infused with appropriate herbs (try elderflower or comfrey for dry hair, lavender or yarrow for greasy hair, burdock root or garlic for dandruff, catmint for an itchy scalp, or southernwood, parsley and other hair tonics) and apply the warm oil for up to half an hour — *before* washing your hair.

Progressive herbal hair colourants include elderberries or indigo with henna for black hair; blue or purple hollyhocks to remove brassiness from grey hair; sage, ivy berries or walnut casing to darken hair; henna, saffron, calendula, red hibiscus or alkanet root to redden it; and camomile, mullein, blue-purple hollyhock flowers, privet leaves, rhubarb root or lemon juice to enhance fair hair.

A hair-dressing recommended in *The Field* in the 19th century included almond oil, clear alcohol, quinine hydrochloride, bay oil and clover oil. Fetch the antimacassars!

Teeth

Clean your teeth with sage leaves, and remove stains with lemon peel or half a wild strawberry. For a toothpaste, combine powdered strawberry root, charcoal or bicarbonate of soda with water and a couple of drops of peppermint oil. Chlorophyll freshens the breath: chew parsley or make a mouthwash of liquidised nettle leaves or watercress, and use peppermint infusions,

rosewater, lavender water or diluted witch hazel as a rinse, or mint and rosemary as an antiseptic. And lodge a clove bud against an aching tooth to deaden the pain.

Eyes

The pretty little plant called eyebright is the traditional remedy for sore or tired eyes: bathe them in a cool infusion made by boiling the freshly picked plant in water. Use herbal tea-bags (camomile, rosehip etc.) or slices of cold cucumber as refreshing eye pads, or check a good herbal book for other useful eyepad decoctions.

Herbal remedies

It is likely that the whole idea of distilling essential plant oils began in the tea pot, and herbal brews of various kinds are still universally used not only as refreshing teas but also for medicinal purposes. For guidance on appropriate herbs and mixtures for different disorders and complaints, consult a reliable herb book (see Bibliography): the range of remedies is enormous and has been built up over thousands of years. It is only very recently that people have turned to drug-dispensing doctors rather than herbalists, and even the most up-to-date pharmaceutical manufacturers are well aware that plants are natural factories of their source material and that the wise-women and witch-doctors knew very well how to use them. Their cures, though often accompanied by psychology, were rooted (literally) in the intrinsic properties of the plants' chemicals.

Please remember that some herbs are very powerful indeed and should be treated with as much respect as any pharmaceutical drug. That is why you should take care to consult an authoritative source before dabbling with their healing powers. All I intend to give you here is an outline of the basic ways of presenting the remedies, and the thought that you could develop a very useful and much needed service to smallholders by specialising in reliable and thoroughly tested herbal and traditional remedies for livestock and pets. Undertake some intriguing research into old agricultural manuals as well as herbals for humans, talk to older farmers, gipsies and present-day homoeopathic practitioners, then responsibly and methodically try out every remedy to see if they work and to eliminate side effects. Many livestock owners are turning against veterinary pharmaceuticals but are understandably wary of herbal remedies which smack of 'witchcraft': it is up to you to prove that your treatments are sound and effective.

A *tea* is an infusion of leaves or flowers in hot water (though plants with highly volatile oils can be soaked in cold water for up to 12 hours instead). Using a lidded container made of china, glass or enamel, bring pure spring water to the boil and leave it to stand for half a minute before sprinkling the herb into it. Let it brew with the lid on for ten minutes, stirring it occasionally, then strain into a cup for drinking.

A *decoction* or tisane is an infusion of bark, seeds, roots, thick stems or other plant parts which need to be crushed or bruised first in order to release their active principles (i.e. the elements within the plant that have an effect on the body). After crushing the hard material, put it in cold water and slowly bring it to the boil, then simmer with the lid off for at least ten minutes to reduce its volume by three-quarters. Take the container off the heat, put the lid on and let it steep and cool for a few minutes before straining.

A *tincture* is a combination of powdered hard materials or chopped fresh herbs steeped in alcohol for medicinal purposes. Put the herbs into alcohol in a tightly lidded container, using something like vodka or brandy (definitely not surgical spirit!). Leave in a warm place for a fortnight, shaking daily, then strain into dark-glass storage jars. Tinctures are used very diluted for homoeopathic remedies, or otherwise either neat or diluted in hot water.

A *syrup* is the combination of a herbal remedy (infusion, decoction, tincture) with honey to make it more palatable: mix the remedy with honey and slowly bring to the boil until it becomes a syrup. It can be stored in the fridge. A *julep* is a sweet drink, often medicated; in America it is often a mixture of mint, ice, sugar and spirits — pure pleasure!

A *maceration* is herbs steeped in oil, vinegar or alcohol, rather than infused in hot water. Crush fresh herbs and put them into a glass jar covered with the chosen medium; seal, and leave for a fortnight, shaking the jar daily, then strain and add fresh herbs. Repeat the process until the liquid smells strongly of the herbs; then strain finally, bottle and seal.

A *compress* is an external application of a remedy, on a clean cloth against the skin. Soak the cloth in a hot infusion or decoction. For a hot compress, apply the cloth as hot as the skin can tolerate and retain the heat with plastic and towels.

A *poultice* is a compress using the actual plant material rather than its infusion or decoction. Crush and mash fresh plant matter and mix it with boiling water to make a pulp, which is applied direct to the skin (when cool enough) as if it was a compress pad.

Fresheners

You can use mixtures of dried herbs and flowerheads to sweeten a room or to freshen linen and clothes, and they smell much better than any manufacturer's air-sprays. As a cottage industry, this could be part of a larger aromatic and decorative range based on dried material and including perhaps dried-flower arrangements, sleep-inducing pillows, potpourri, incense and plant-based insect repellents. The fun lies in selecting your mixtures for different applications and in presenting them in attractive containers, be they bags, baskets, boxes, china, earthenware or crystal.

Aromatics are ideal point-of-sale goods. They can lure customers from a distance by their smell and they can also appeal to the eye. An open basketful of aromatic petals is pretty enough without any further decoration, just waiting to be scooped into plain paper bags, but herb leaves would sell better in imaginatively designed containers. Prepare an appealing mail-order catalogue as well, with good illustrations and well-written descriptions. Aromatics are so *evocative*: make full use of their emotional triggers in your advertising. The genius who bagged up potpourri mixtures for sweetening the privy and called it the Jakesack deserves recognition for the name, even if it was borrowed from Shakespeare.

Incense

Lavender incense is the simplest and perhaps most traditional way of sweetening cottage rooms. Simply dry some lavender stems thoroughly and then burn them like joss sticks: they will smoulder gently and waft out the pervading lavender smoke. Burn them steadily and slowly in a bunch, or put dried lavender flowers in a perforated metal dish to smoulder as you carry it about the place.

Lavender is a good ingredient in moth-repellent sachets (add dried tansy, southern-wood, rosemary, pennyroyal, poisonous stavesacre seeds, patchouli oil and camphor) and is also said to repel cabbage-white butterflies and rabbits from your kitchen garden. Don't believe it! Whites adore lavender and flock to it in their dozens, so it will probably attract them from miles around rather than disguise the alluring smell of the brassicas.

All sorts of aromatic plants, resins and spices can be used as incense or perhaps as insecticides. For something more sophisticated than lavender sticks, you need a combustible base of pure willow charcoal, combustion aids (either saltpetre or sugar — but not together), fragrances (resins, bay leaves, lavender and other flowers, thyme or rosemary leaves etc.), essential oils and fixatives, and a binding agent like gum mucilage to bind all the powdered dry ingredients which you have ground to a fine dust. Mix the powders, oils and mucilage to a pliable paste and knead it; form into little cones or pastilles and dry them in a dark, airy place. That's all there is to it, apart from selecting a pleasing mixture. For joss

sticks, wrap the paste around thin wooden splints to dry.

Pomanders

These are also very simple to make: just press cloves into an orange and then roll it in a mixture of orris root powder with allspice or cinnamon. It should retain its scent for about a year. But that is not a real pomander, or 'amber apple', which is a perfumed ball, often elaborately decorated. The ball might be orange-sized, or it might be a lampshade bobble, or perfumed beads strung into necklaces, bracelets and belts. Originally the pomander was made from ambergris or fragrant resins like gum benjamin (benzoin, from a Sumatran tree), labdanum (resin from Mediterranean cistus leaves) or storax (from the liquidambar tree). The resins are ground together and melted; add finely powdered spices like orris root, spikenard, cloves, aloes wood or cinnamon and a fixative (ambergris) and knead it all together. Beads can be made in moulds or rolled into shape before the mixture sets and pierced with a hot needle so that they can be threaded later.

The idea of fragrant jewellery is a pleasant one. The pomander beads could be combined with ordinary decorative beads in glass, silver, semiprecious stones etc., or interspersed with little pieces of nutmeg set in silver clasps and fragrant seeds and woods, with perhaps a few rose-petal beads (which are rather laborious to make: spread the petals in a warm, airy, shaded place until dry but not crisp, roll individually on a darning needle, with the base of the petal innermost, and fasten with a little gum). You could make larger beads and turn them on a lathe or carve them. Or you could make insect-repellent medallions, or gentle sleep-inducing bedhead decorations, or large room pomanders decorated with ribbons and pearls . . .

Hop pillows

The growing of hops is described in the Brewhouse section — hop flowers are preservatives used to clarify and flavour beer but they are also good as mild sedatives and have a gently somniferous or narcotic effect. Use them in bath water to relax, or drink a bedtime cup of hop tea, or dry the flowers for a sleep-encouraging pillow or underpillow sachet if you like the smell. Be warned, however, that some people find hops increase existing depression. Several other herbs make soothing pillows — bergamot, valerian, camomile, catnip or sweet marjoram, with some lavender to counteract sadness. Once you become interested in herbs, you will discover just how important aromatics can be in everyday life: each has a different effect on senses, moods and emotions and all you need is the scent of them.

Potpourri
Potpourri is ideal for mood relief as well as being a room freshener, and the making of it is as individual as the blending of a new perfume or whisky. Rose petals are traditionally at the core of potpourri. Choose the fragrant old-fashioned varieties — cabbage roses, damask roses and so on — and gather their petals on a dry day, after a few days of fine weather. Only pick freshly opened, undamaged blooms and gather them in the morning after the dew has left them completely. Use other flowers as well, for their fragrance or their colour, either as petals or as whole heads picked as the buds are just opening. Spread them out to dry on tissue paper or stretched muslin in a shady, well ventilated place for perhaps a week, until they are crisp but not disintegrating. Rosebuds can be dried intact, completely covered under very fine silver sand (or sugar) and in full sun for a couple of weeks or more.

Other ingredients might include dried aromatic leaves, ground or freshly grated spices, crushed dried roots, citrus peel, fragrant wood shavings and essential oils. You also need fixatives to hold the scents by absorbing them so that the life of the potpourri is increased: try violet-scented orris root powder, vanilla-scented gum bezoin, sandalwood, myrrh, chipre, frankincense and so on.

There are two methods of making potpourri: the moist and the dry. The dry method is simpler but moist potpourri will last for years. To make dry potpourri, simply dry and mix all your selected ingredients, with a little coarse bay salt as a preservative, and add a fixative, stirring it all together with your fingers, then add essential oils drop by drop. Store it in a sealed container in a dark, warm, dry place like an airing cupboard for about six weeks to cure, then transfer it to open bowls or sachets for use. The moist method involves packing alternate layers of partially dried rose petals (to the texture of leather) with uniodised sea salt, pressing down each layer firmly with a plate, and leaving the whole lot in a sealed container for at least two months to cure and form a moist, scented cake. Flake the rose cake with your fingers and add dry herbs, grated spices and resins, and other moist salted flowers, then cure again for several weeks before finally adding decorative dried flowers and essential oils. There are numerous recipes for both methods.

It can be much simpler. In 1989, for the first time since it was planted as a dry stick ten years earlier, my indoor frangipani flowered. When the heavily perfumed flowers faded one by one and dropped of their own accord, I let them lie there on the windowsill to dry unassisted until they became brown and leathery. More than a year later they still wafted their rich scent into the room. (No, the plant has not flowered again — yet.)

Pest deterrents
For your own use (and the ingenious might be able to devise marketable products), Table 3 suggests herbs which will repel certain insects and rodents. It is in most cases enough simply to leave a few sprigs of the herb lying around — or you could include them in potpourri or sachets.

Decorations
Many of the herbal items already described are decorative as well as aromatic or useful. Dried flowers are an obvious extension to

your activities (methods are in the Garden section) and you could also preserve leaves. Autumn foliage can be ironed, but a better method is to pick small branches of leaves just as the autumn colour is beginning to show and then soak them in glycerine. Slit the base of the stems and stand them in warm water to encourage sap movement before transferring them to a warm glycerine solution (1 part glycerine to 2 parts boiling water, mixed well and cooled somewhat) in a narrow container so that the bottom 4 in of stems are immersed. Let them stand in the solution until drops of glycerine appear on the leaves, showing that they are saturated; it takes anything from a couple of days to perhaps three weeks. Take them out and wipe off the excess oil from the leaves.

Leaf skeletons are made by soaking the leaf in cold water until its top skin rots. Then lay the leaf flat on a board and very gently scrape away the tissues until only the lacelike skeleton remains. The job is quicker if you add a little washing soda to water and gently simmer the immersed leaf for an hour or so before scraping. Finally, dry the skeleton and press it between sheets of blotting paper.

Fresh flowers can also be pressed in blotting paper — but sterilise it first or they will go mouldy. Thicken the wad with layers of newspaper, put it in a flowerpress and pop it in a microwave oven for a couple of minutes; leave it to cool for two hours or so before unscrewing the press. It's much quicker than using the Encyclopaedia Britannica or telephone directories and bricks.

Use pressed flowers to make pictures, cards, frames and so on. For serious card production, invest in a hot sealing machine to glaze the work with transparent film.

Pressed leaves, flowers and grasses can also decorate items such as wastepaper baskets and parchment lampshades (under varnish or film) or you can make original fingerplates for doors by cutting a clear perspex plate to shape, drilled with holes for the fixing screws, and putting it as a wipe-clean surface over a design of pressed plant material mounted on a piece of card of the same shape.

The brewhouse

Just to make your mouth water, in Table 4 (below) are some of the alcoholic concoctions you might make from hedgerow and garden produce.

TABLE 4

Brews

WINES		CORDIALS AND LIQUEURS	ALES ETC.
Apple wine	English		Apelsaft
Bee wine	grape	Blackberry cordial	Barleywater
Blackberry	Gooseberry	(for coughs)	Beer
Birch	Gorse	Cherry brandy	Cider
Cherry, morello	Japanese	Elderberry syrup	Ginger beer
Cowslip	rice	Elderflower cordial	Hot Lambswool
Crab apple	Mangel	Hawthorn brandy	Mead
Currant, black	wurzel	Old Jenny	Nettle beer
Currant, red	Oak	Peach brandy	Perry
Currant,	Parsley	Raspberry vinegar	Root beer
white	Parsnip	Rosehip syrup	Scrumpy
Damson	Raisin	Sloe gin	Spruce beer
Elderberry	Raspberry	Verjuice	
Elderflower	Rosehip	Whisky cream liqueur	
	Rowan		

Hedgerow hops growing wild and flowering.

Hops

The hop is a perennial vine with fast-growing annual shoots. It can be propagated from early-summer cuttings of the young shoots or from seed, or by dividing the roots and suckers of female plants. Grow hops in a sunny, open position in a deep, fertile soil, setting the plants about a stride apart and supporting them with canes and wires. The most valuable part of the plant is the female flower, which presents an argument against propagation by seed because you will not know if the plant is female for a couple of years. Male flowers, which are produced on separate plants, can be lightly boiled and added to salads.

The original use for the hop was medicinal: it is a tonic and a diuretic as well as a sedative. It is also used to give taste to beer: the female flower's essential oils are the bitter flavour of the brew. The dried flowers, harvested ripe in the autumn, also clarify and preserve the beer but, right up to the 16th century, English brewers preferred to use alecost and ground ivy as they firmly believed that hops induced melancholy. The flowers should be used within a few months of drying, before their flavour becomes unpleasant.

An infusion makes a relaxing bath additive but a better use for the flowers is sprinkled with alcohol and sewn into little sleep-inducing pillows. They can also be infused as a mildly sedative tea to combat digestive problems, or as an antiseptic. The leaves are rather bitter but can be blanched for kitchen use or boiled to make a brown dye. The young sideshoots can be steamed and served like asparagus. The stems, gathered in late autumn, can be converted into paper and cloth or used for wickerwork.

Basic brewing

'The art of brewing consists in a knowledge of conducting that process by which the saccharine or sweet matter contained in many vegetable substances may be extracted, and partly converted into spirit, or alcohol, by fermentation, the addition of various substances for the purpose of giving flavour, retarding fermentation after it has arrived at a certain point, and the separation of the fermentable matter so perfectly as to leave the liquor clear. In this state it forms Porter, strong as Table Beer, according to the peculiarity of management, or the strength derived from the sweet matter.'

Thus was it written in Baxter in the 1830s, followed at very great length indeed by an explanation of the principles of fermentation (a veritable chemistry lesson) and by a statement that 'substances generally employed in the making of beer are water, malt and hops', but that it could also be made from unmalted grain, cane sugar, parsnips, beet, Indian corn stalks or certain sweet grasses.

Here, broadly, are Baxter's beer-making principles. Whether the water is hard or soft is a matter of personal preference: both will extract the 'sweet matter'. To sweeten the grain (which should be barley), it must be malted and it must be malting rather than feed barley: put it in a non-metal container, cover with soft rainwater and let it soak for two or three days, then strain and spread the grain on wooden trays (or a clean floor) in a temperature of 50°F (10°C), leaving it for at least ten days to sprout — turn it twice a day until you see small rootlets. These are the malt and need to be separated by drying the grain slowly in an oven at less than 180°F until the rootlets part from the grain (they should be crisp and sweet, tasting rather like toffee) and can be sifted out and coarsely ground.

If you use cane sugar, you should be able to dispense with all that malting business. The French, in Baxter's time, used starchy potatoes instead of malted barley; some English home brewers used parsnips, beet or mangel wurzel, all of which were sweet enough to ferment easily.

Enough of sweetness: you want bitterness, and that is where the hop-flowers come in, though Baxter was wary of their 'stupefying' effect. He urged caution during the brewing process in case the brewer was overcome by the soporific effects of the hops. Apparently all sorts of substances were being used, mostly illegally, rather than hops — including wormwood, bitter oranges, Seville rind and gentian root.

The important points to remember were to pay great heed to temperature and specific gravity (using a thermometer and a saccharometer). The main stages were the extraction of saccharine from the malted grain or other matter, the flavouring with hops, the fermentation of the saccharine matter and the separation of the fermented liquor from the yeast or fermentable matter. Here's how:

Put the malt and water into a warm mashing tub at 170°F, then mash and stir it for fifteen minutes; add more water at 180–185°F, cover and let it stand for up to four hours. Then draw off the clear wort and boil it to concentrate and clarify. Add hops to the boiling wort after an hour and continue to boil for another thirty minutes, then sieve and cool quickly. When it is cool, add yeast and mix it in carefully, then let it ferment. (It will start working more quickly if you habitually use a brewer's besom which gradually becomes impregnated with yeast through successive brews.) Skim until no more yeast rises then check the process of fermentation before it turns into vinegar: beat it up and separate off into casks.

Ginger beer
First start a 'plant'. Put 2oz baker's yeast into a jar and add two cupfuls of water, 2tspn sugar and 2tspn powdered ginger. Feed the plant daily for a week with a teaspoonful each of ginger and sugar. To make ginger beer, drain off the plant liquid through muslin (and keep the residue to be split in half and start two new plants). Add the juice of two lemons, two pints of boiling water and a pound of sugar to the liquid, making it up to a gallon with water. Leave it for three hours, then bottle. Drink it after six days.

Nettle beer
Into a pan put 2gal young nettle tops (washed), 2gal water, half an ounce of root ginger, four pounds of malt, 2oz hops and (optional) 4oz sarsparilla. Bring to the boil, simmer for 15 minutes, strain into an earthenware crock containing more than a pound of sugar and stir to dissolve. Use a little of the liquor to beat an ounce of brewer's yeast to a frothy cream and add it to the mixture when it is lukewarm. Cover and leave until it begins to ferment, then bottle it and tie the cork down. Ready to drink after 12 hours.

Mead
Primitive mead was naturally fermented by fungal spores in old rye-straw hives: it was

simply the washings from the combs after the honey had dripped out and the wax was extracted in a hot water bath, which left you with honey-and-water 'swish-swash', to which pepper and spice were added. For a better brew of mead, you need fresh, ripe honey, preferably light in colour. Dissolve four or five pounds of honey to every gallon of water and boil for up to 45 minutes, then skim off the froth or scum. Pour the liquid into a cask or earthenware jar, filling to the brim. When it is lukewarm, add an ounce of brewer's yeast per gallon (liquefy it first) and let it ferment in a warm place at 65–70°F. When the bubbling stops, add quarter of an ounce of isinglass per gallon. Cork or bung tight, store in a cool, dry place and wait for six months before bottling off. For variety, before boiling, add thinly sliced lemon peel and, for a tangy brew, also add an ounce of hops and half an ounce of crushed ginger root per gallon. It can also be fortified with brandy, or blended with herbs and spices to make medicinal metheglin.

Spruce beer
Collect green shoots of *Pinus sylvestris* in the spring and put them in a preserving pan. Cover with water and boil to extract the resinous flavour: the water will turn deep brown. Strain, boil again to reduce the volume by half, bottle and store. This is the 'essence'.

Now make the 'spruce'. Dissolve two pounds of black treacle (or molasses or coarse brown sugar) in a gallon of water, warming it slightly. Put it into a cask or earthenware jar and add another gallon of cold spring water, 2 tbspn of the essence and half an ounce of brewer's yeast when it is tepid. Stir, and allow to ferment in a warm place (70°F) for a few days. When bubbling finishes, bung tight and store in a cool place. It will be ready to drink a week or two later.

For a white beer, use loafsugar or honey as the sweetener.

Cider
Cider (a word with Hebrew roots) has been drunk here since the 11th century and is especially a brew of southern England,

which is ideal apple-growing country. Perry is in effect cider made from fermented pear juice.

In the 1830s there were two recognised kinds of cider: harsh, strong scrumpy and mild, sweet cider. Of the sweet ciders the main varieties were that of Herefordshire, which was stronger, more highly coloured but less sweet than that of Devon and Somerset, which was pale and extremely sweet, especially in the parish of Kingston, near Taunton, where the best cider was made. Much of the difference between the harsh and the mild lies in checking the fermentation process before too much of the apple sugar is converted into spirit: the later the checking, the harsher and stronger the drink.

When apple juice is first squeezed, it is a milky green colour but within minutes of exposure to the air it becomes yellowish brown and sweeter. Sweetness depends substantially on the variety of apple and also the season: the same tree can yield sweeter apples in some seasons than in others. A dry season favours sweetness, a wet one juiciness.

In the 1950s typical English cider-making apples included the bitter-sweets like Chisel Jersey, Knotted Kernel, Major and Royal Wilding, the sweet White Jersey, Sweet Alford and Sweet Coppin, and the sharp or sour Cap of Liberty, Foxwhelp, Ponsford, Reinette Obry and that old favourite, the Kingston Black. Today, Somerset cider-makers can still find Chisel Jersey and others like Tremlett's Bitter, Porter's Perfection, Brown Snout, Dabinett, Yarlington Mill and Somerset Red Streak. What a relief to hear such names — and such a variety of names — in an age when most of our commercial eating-apple orchards and super-markets offer only a handful of different apples. A century ago Britain had 1500 varieties of apple.

The secret of cider-making is in the blending of different types of apple and in how the juice is treated. In general, rich, sweet apples make the better cider, though 'cider apples' are notoriously sharp and a proportion of acidity is necessary. The famous Kingston cider of the early 19th century was made from Kingston Blacks, which combined bitterness with sweetness. Aim for a mixture of sweet and sour apples, with a greater proportion of the former for most tastes. However, for a dry cider you need more sour apples.

According to a 19th-century American recipe, for a richer cider choose apples with juice of the greatest specific gravity: they have more sugar in them. The best seem to have red skins and yellow pulp (often tough and fibrous); if the rind and pulp are green, the cider will be colourless, weak and thin.

It is important to pick the apples which hang longest on the tree: cider should be made as late in the year as possible. Harvest in November rather than October, since a cold season is better for controlling fermentation. Pick them when they are dry

and perfectly ripe, and all of equal ripeness in the batch. They should be beginning to fall off the tree. The traditional method of harvesting was to knock the apples down with a long pole, but inevitably many were thereby bruised and partially decayed before use, which was not good for the flavour of the cider. It would be better to shake them gently off the tree at intervals when they are ready, catching them as they fall, then pile them on the ground in small heaps out of doors for two or three weeks to mature the juice and thus increase the strength and flavour. Be careful to reject any rotten fruit and to remove foreign matter before grinding.

Cider-making can be quite simple or extremely complicated, and if you read Baxter (1830s) on the subject you will feed your apples to the pigs rather than try the

Cider mill and press.

'scientific' processes described. Basically, however, it involves pulping, pressing, fermentation, checking the fermentation, racking and bottling. You can pulp the apples in a wooden tub by hand (or foot), or grind them West Country style between a pair of wooden teethed rollers or fluted iron rollers set close enough together to bruise every kernel, or heavy stone mills if you can find them.

Now the pulp (or musk) needs to be pressed. In Somerset, the tradition was to press it immediately after crushing, and convert it into 'cider cheese', which was a square mess of alternate layers of ground apples and clean wheat straw or horsehair cloths. The wooden press was tightened by a large screw so that a stream of reddish, muddy, very sweet liquor ran out. The pressure was gradually increased until the juice ceased to flow and a large, flat cake of pulp remained. The cake was cut around the edges with a hay-knife and pressed again; and this process was repeated three or four times until every precious drop of juice had been extracted and transferred into casks to ferment.

Ideally, the casks should be of well-seasoned oak. Fill them up with the juice, leaving the bungs out: the cider will overflow during the fermentation and you should keep the casks topped up. You could bung the cask immediately but it is more than likely that the whole lot would explode!

The fermentation process will cease naturally after a few weeks and at that stage it is 'harsh cider', which can be bunged down for use (seal the bungs with resin and beeswax). However, in most cases you want to arrest the fermentation before it reaches that stage: don't let it decompose more than a quarter of the original sugar in the liquor. So leave it working for only a few days in a vat, skimming off the froth, and then turn it into casks, bunging them closely but with a half-inch syphon through the bung to let the gas escape in due course. The outer arm of the syphon should run into a glass of water on top of the cask: as soon as you see the first bubble of gas in the water, it is time for racking. Keep a glassful of liquor outside

the cask so that you can watch its progress in a visible double-check. One way of halting the fermentation is 'stumming' or matching the cask by pouring a pailful or two of cider into an empty cask, then lowering in a burning piece of thick linen smeared with sulphur; bung the cask tightly to let a sulphurous gas form, then fill the cask with cider and let it settle a few days before racking off.

Real experts put an ear to the cask to listen for 'singing' — a kind of hissing caused by the small bubbles of gas reaching a crescendo — and as soon as they hear it, they rack the contents into another cask, leaving the dregs behind. Perfectionists will rack up to twenty times, or only four or five times if they have used a mixture of isinglass, sour cider and fresh calcined plaster of Paris powder or sulphate of lime, filtered through fine calico, to clarify the cider.

Twelve months later (which will be the second April after the apples were harvested) you can bottle the cider, adding a raisin or a lump of white sugar to make it 'brisk'. Wire down the corks and wait for another year before it is fit to drink.

Cider vinegar

Either ferment pressed apple juice with molasses in a warm place, or let some cider stand in barrels with the bunghole open until its second fermentation is complete (after several months), exposing as large an area to the air as possible. If you dripped the cider through beechwood shavings, the vinegar could be ready in days rather than months. *Verjuice* is a vinegar made from the juice of crab-apples.

Cider brandy

Calvados and Applejack are cider brandies. If you want to make cider brandy commercially, you will need a licence and the tax accounting is quite complicated. The first such licence in two centuries was issued recently to organic farmer Julian Temperley of Kingsbury Episcopi in Somerset, who already had twenty years of experience in making dry cider using some of the old apple varieties. It is unlikely that you can compete but, broadly, you must first make your cider and then use your still and your skill to convert it into 70 per cent alcohol. Mature it in the cask for three years. From twenty pounds of apples you could get one bottle of brandy and it will be ready to drink five years after they were harvested.

You might like to experiment with cherry brandy: pack lots of morello cherries into an earthenware container, sprinkle them with crushed brown sugar candy, fill up with brandy and leave for several months before bottling. More original is hawthorn brandy liqueur: stand hawthorn flowers, sugar and brandy in a warm sun and then in the airing cupboard for three months before gently decanting.

Wines

If you have no experience of country wine-making, start with an all-in-one kit from Boots to learn about the principles. Genuine wine is, of course, made from the produce of the vine but similar fermentations of a wide range of fruit, leaves and roots are also called 'wine', though many would say that only the grape has the right proportions of the substances needed for true wine — sugar, 'ferment', acids and water. The difference between various grape wines lies in the different proportions of these constituents in the 'must' and also the different methods of managing fermentation to achieve dry and strong, or sweet and light, or brisk wine or, at the worst, vinegar.

As with cider, the more complete the fermentation, the more the sugar is decomposed and the drier the wine. To prolong fermentation in the pursuit of dryness, mix back the settled lees and the natural yeast into the wine. For a sweet wine, however, let the yeast rise and flow out through the bung holes and keep the lees as separate as possible from the wine. Racking or drawing off separates a lot of the leaven; clarification precipitates more of it (add isinglass, which will soon collect at the bottom, carrying leaven with it). Sulphuring can separate out what remains.

Wine-making is truly an art and likely to become a lifelong passion once you start, whether with grapes from your own vineyard (and that is an expensive, long-term enterprise) or with hedgerow harvests to make country wines. The broad principles apply, whatever the basic materials, except that if you are using something other than grapes you will probably need to compensate for the raw juice's imbalance of the constituents — you might need to add sugar, increase the tartarous acids (the sweeter the fruit, the more cream of tartar you need) or reduce the malic acid.

The first rule is never to use metallic vessels at any stage of any winemaking process. Fermentation should be in wooden, earthenware or glass containers. Another hint is that you should always choose cool, serene weather when clarifying, racking and bottling. The two important terms are the 'must', which is the juice prepared for fermentation, and the 'ferment', which is the leaven present naturally in most vegetable substances and is of course necessary for fermentation. If you let grapejuice rest at an appropriate temperature, fermentation takes place and a substance separates out during the process, settling at the bottom. When it settles, fermentation stops and will not start again unless the sediment is stirred back into the liquor.

There are countless recipes for country wines — some of them in books mentioned in the Bibliography, many more in very old magazines or memories. Experiment widely before trying to sell your wines, and make sure that you can achieve at least some degree of consistency so that your customers know what to expect. Bottle and label them beautifully and then get on with the business of marketing. The following recipes are merely to give you some idea of the basic processes which you can apply to many other garden or hedgerow raw materials.

Gooseberry wine
Use unripe fruit, with not even a hint of ripening but at full growth. The green Bath variety is ideal if you can find it and you should avoid types which are highly flavoured when ripe.

Country wines from Lurgashall.

Discard bruised or otherwise unsound fruit and bits of stalk, blossom and whatnot. Put the fruit into a clean tub and bruise it deliberately, applying enough pressure to burst without actually crushing the berries or materially compressing the skins. Add water at the rate of a gallon to ten pounds of fruit; stir, squeeze by hand until all the juice and pulp are separated from solid matter. Let it rest for up to 24 hours then strain it forcefully through a coarse bag. Pour a little fresh water through the husks to flush out the last of the soluble matter.

In the juice of the original ten pounds of fruit, dissolve six to eight pounds of white sugar and add water to bulk it up to two and a half gallons. Now you have the equivalent of a grape 'must'.

Put the must into a big tub, cover it with a blanket or cloth and stand it in a temperature of 55–60°F for up to 24 hours so that it begins to ferment, then draw off into casks for the fermentation process: fill to the bunghole so that the scum can flow off, and keep topping up as necessary. When the hissing noise of fermentation diminishes, bung the cask but have a hole beside it with a wooden peg so that you can loosen the peg after a few days to release gas if necessary. Do so at intervals until there seems to be no further danger of excessive gas, then tighten it permanently. Leave in a cool cellar all winter; check in February or March to see if it is ready for bottling, or decant into a fresh cask at the end of December to clear the first lees and taste for sweetness, stirring up the lees if it is too sweet (do this in clear, dry, cold weather), then bottle it in March.

Gooseberry champagne is gooseberry wine to which brandy, whisky, sherry or madeira have been added when the first fermentation ceases; then cask for six months, bottle, and stand for another six months before drinking. It will be bubbly, and you need a bottle of brandy to every five gallons of gooseberry must.

Similar steps are followed for other garden berries. For *red currant* wine, to eight gallons of berries try adding a quart of raspberries and two pounds of thinly sliced beetroot, then after fermentation add a gallon of brandy, stand for a week, rack off and stand for another two months before finally racking off, casking and bunging — this can be stored in a cool place for many years. For *white currant* wine, add a gallon of gooseberries and two ounces of bitter almonds to nine gallons of currants and then proceed as for red currant. For *black currant*, add three gallons of strawberries to six gallons of currants. For *elderberry*, add ginger root and bitter almonds to infuse and then remove them. Add bruised ginger root and sugar to *rowan* berries, and add an eighth of their own broken stones for *damson* or *cherry* wine. Add cider, lemon rind and orange rind to *strawberries* and also to *raspberries* (along with the juice of red and white currants for the latter). For *rosehips*, boil them in water with ginger, orange and lemon slices and then stand for three days, stirring daily, before straining and adding sugar, yeast and lemon juice; cask, bung three days later and leave for three months before bottling or drinking. These are all suggestions — experiment!

Blackberry wine

This is a simple recipe. Stand alternate layers of blackberries and sugar in wide-mouthed jars for three weeks, then strain and bottle the liquid with a raisin or two, corking it lightly at first and more tightly later. It will keep for a year.

Parsnip wine

Use clean, chopped roots and boil them in soft spring water until tender. Put in a wooden vessel and add best pale argol (crude tartar of wine) and sugar, plus a couple of ounces of wheat flour or potato starch and a little salt to assist fermentation if necessary. Make the wine in March, rack it after Christmas, add isinglass the following March and bottle it then or keep it in the wood until next Christmas. It is very potent. You can also make *mangel wurzel* wine: four pounds of sliced roots to a gallon of water with an ounce or so of ginger, boiled together until tender; strain off the juice and to each gallon add three pounds of sugar, half an ounce of yeast and the juice of three oranges. Ferment in a brimful container, topping up for four or five weeks until the bubbling stops. Stir, leave for three days, then strain into casks or bottles and store for ·at least five months.

Cowslip wine

I hardly dare give you this one — the flowers are much too precious. But it will serve for other flower wines. Use freshly picked blossoms (no stalks or green calyces) and soak each pound in six gallons of water for 48 hours, then strain. Add three pounds of sugar to the gallon plus the thin peel of eight Seville oranges and eight lemons; boil for half an hour, cool to lukewarm and add a tablespoonful of yeast. Stand for three days, skim, ferment in casks, and bung tightly once the fermentation has ceased. Bottle in twelve months: it will be drinkable three months later.

Elderflower champagne

Pick the flowers on a dry, sunny day when they are full of pollen (the main yeast source). Put boiling water into a sterilised container and add sugar at one and a half pounds to the gallon. Dissolve the sugar, cool, then add lemon juice and rind, two tablespoons of vinegar (cider or wine) and the flowers. Cover with muslin and leave for 24 hours, then strain and bottle. You can drink it (chilled) after a fortnight.

Some people add beaten egg-white in the first stage and an ounce of yeast and a raisin with the flowers, and then stir daily for ten days before straining into loosely corked stone jars until fermentation is complete, then corking tightly and leaving for six months before drinking.

Birch wine

An acquired taste! Tap birch trees for sap in coldish, windy weather in March. To a gallon of sap add three pounds of sugar, a pound of raisins and an ounce of almonds; boil for half an hour, skimming off the scum. Leave to cool and add a teaspoon of yeast when tepid. Let it ferment under cover for three or four days; remove scum, transfer to cask or jar (filled to the brim) and leave to ferment again for up to four weeks until fermentation ceases, topping up as necessary. Bung tight or bottle off and store in a cool dark place to mature for at least three months.

Oak wine is made from the leaves. Boil three and a half pounds of honey per gallon of water for 45 minutes and pour the hot liquid over three dozen sound oak leaves. Stand for half a day, strain off and add a teaspoon of yeast per gallon. Leave to ferment in a warm room for three or four days then pour into casks or bottle; seal, and stand for 3–6 months before using.

Sloe gin

Put pricked or first-frost sloes into a bottling jar and fill up with gin (expensive!). Cork and store in a warm, dark cupboard. It will be ready by Christmas but is better later. Some people add an equal weight of sugar.

Kitchencraft

You can only compete in the kitchen if you can offer interesting foods of very high quality, preferably from homegrown organic produce or traditional livestock breeds, giving your wares an evocative name and presenting them beautifully: little touches do mean a lot. To make a successful cottage industry from the kitchen, remember that you cannot compete directly with large-scale producers: the whole point is to produce something different, individual, tasty, pure and genuine. Victorian or older cookery books should be able to inspire you but you

also need to consider such modern requirements as food regulations: consult your local environmental health officer if you intend to offer converted produce for sale.

Table 5 (opposite) offers some suggestions, many of them culled from the inspiring *British Country Foods Directory*, from which you will see that there are plenty of flourishing kitchen-based cottage industries in Britain. In the face of such high-class competition, presentation is vital and, for a real luxury, how about a handmade wicker hamper with a Jacob-wool picnic rug?

Bakery

For a complete enterprise, grow your own grain organically, mill it yourself and then bake it. That will be a great deal of hard work. (In The Gambia, small diesel-powered mills have recently liberated village women whose time can now be spent tending crops and livestock rather than endlessly grinding corn.)

For a while I lived in a converted watermill which had served the valley for two centuries: not only had the local grain been milled there well into the 1920s but they also had a kitchen bakery where, within living memory, bread and doughnuts were baked at the mill and then delivered, warm from the oven, in one of those early motor vans whose replicas are now seen again in the streets as tradesmen's vehicles. If you are fortunate enough to find a genuine watermill, incidentally, you might have the extra bonus of harvestable eels and crayfish in the millpond, and perhaps a small trout enterprise as a sideline, and certainly the pleasure of the company of ducks galore, but you need to handle an awful lot of grain to make best use of the machinery.

It is difficult to work out the economics but, if you can, it would certainly be satisfying to take it all the way, working the land with horses for grain production, milling and baking on the premises, and delivery as well. It will take up more hours than you ever knew existed and your prices will have to be high: it would be safer to have a direct link with reliable retail outlets such as hotels, restaurants and village shops than to deliver to every household in the parish! However, growing and milling organic grain to sell as flour is a proven practical enterprise, and so, as a venture on its own, is high quality bakery. It's the combining of them that will overwhelm you.

Juices

Invest in a good juice extractor. There is an interesting one from Finland which doubles up as a steamer: the juices are released by steam rather than by pressing, and are already pasteurised. You could specialise in orchard and hedgerow juices with a real country flavour, selling in sealed, sterilised bottles, or experiment with freezing perhaps.

Preserves

A lot of people, supported by a long tradition of kitchencraft, produce preserves for use at home or for sale through small country outlets such as the local WI market. Why not sell in the cities, or by mail order? To turn such skills into a cottage industry,

---

TABLE 5

Food

BAKERY	CONFECTIONERY	Buttermilk	Basil sauce
Shortbread	Fudge	Flower cheeses	Nut oils
Fruitcake	Toffee	Yarg and nettle	Apple/pear spreads
Christmas cake	Chocolates	Feta	
Christmas pudding	Truffles	Cheesecake	
Steamed puddings	Easter eggs	Ethnic dairy	MEAT/FISH/
Rum tarts	Marshmallows	products	POULTRY
Oatcakes	Coconut ice	Dried milk	Smoked (beef,
Fruit/nut loaves	Boiled sweets	Breed cheeses	venison, pork,
Raised pies	Turkish delight	Ewe butter	Herdwick ham,
Fruit tarts	Rose/violet sweets	Toasted goat's	game, turkey,
Butter biscuits	Mints	cheese	chicken, rabbit,
Brownies	Medlar comfits		duck, shellfish,
Savoury biscuits	Humbugs		trout, eels, prawns,
Wheat wafers	Liquorice	PRESERVES	quail's eggs)
Crunchy cookies	Sherbet	Flavoured mustards	Sausages (goat,
Angel cake	Candied berries	Unexpected	venison, pork)
Walnut cake	Candied flowers	marmalades	Veniburgers
Brandysnaps	Caramels	Chutney, pickles	Goose (ovenready)
Gingerbread men		Sauces	Poulet Noir
Wedding cakes		Hedgerow jams/	Soay lamb
High-fibre cereal	DAIRY	jellies	Chicken (cornfed,
Pasties	Frozen goat/	Wildflower honey	marinated etc.)
Vegan bakes	sheep milk	Liqueur fruits	Unusual eggs
Frozen stoneground	Milkshakes	Bottled fruit	Home-cured
pastry	Cream	Vinegars	ham/bacon
	Butter		Fresh kid/wild boar/
	Cheeses	FRUIT AND	pigeon/guineafowl
	Yogurt	VEGETABLES	Pâté (all sorts —
BEVERAGES	Ice-cream	Alfalfa sprouts	e.g. goat and garlic)
Fresh-frozen juices	Junket	Watercress	Potted fish
Natural spring water	Eggnog	Watercress soup	Eels, mussels, crayfish
Natural seltzer	Milk lollies	Garlic	Snails
water	Milk puddings	Fruit sorbets	Unusual fish
Vanilla water	Beestings	Pumpkin pie	Meat from rare breeds
Carrot juice			

you need originality as well as marketing skills — and again you might look to the hedgerows, or incorporate a regional or historical theme in your marketing. Here are a few ideas to get your imagination working.

Rose-petal jam. Simmer strongly scented red rose petals in water with syrup, lemon-juice and rosewater.

Rosehip syrup. Delicious, evocative, extremely rich in vitamin C (twenty times more than oranges, by weight, and four times as much as black currants). Laborious in the harvesting and preparation — even commercial producers still rely on volunteers or penny-rate school children to pick wild hips. The hairs are skin irritants (basis of childish itching powder). Maybe *elderberry syrup* would be easier, or *mulberry*. How about *herb syrups*? Herb or fruit syrups can also be the basis for jellies, sauces and drinks.

Hedgerows jams and jellies can be much more exciting to the palate than mass-produced preserves. Experiment with hawthorn, rowan, crab apple, rosehip, sloe. Or use unusual garden fruits like *medlar* and *quince* (quince cheese).

Herb jellies are a good accompaniment to, say, toasted goat's cheese, cold meats, roasts or salads. Boil together some chopped crab apples or cooking apples with wine vinegar, water and fresh herbs; drip through a jellybag; add sugar to the juice and boil to setting point. An incidental tip: try tarragon mayonnaise with your plaice or sole — just chop good tarragon into homemade mayonnaise.

Vinegars can be made from fruit (delicious with savoury dishes and, in the case of raspberry and blackberry, useful cough mixtures), herbs (good in salad dressings) or flowers (for cosmetics, perhaps). True fruit vinegars are made from pure juice allowed to ferment. Floral and herbal vinegars can be made more easily by bruising the fresh material and adding warm vinegar to it in a jar. Cap it, stand it on a sunny windowledge for a fortnight (shaking it daily), then strain and store. As a marketing aid, slip a whole fresh sprig of the herb or flower into the bottle: it looks pretty and it identifies the contents at a glance.

Crystallised flowers are easily made: dip them into lightly frothed eggwhite and then into caster sugar; put between sheets of greaseproof paper on a wire rack in an airing cupboard or low oven (with its door ajar) to dry. *Candied barberries*: boil sugar to syrup point, dip the berries in and leave them there for a few hours; lift them out, reboil to candy stage and put the berries in again, leaving them to candy. Do you remember parma violet sweets from child-hood? Can you tell me how to make them? There are lots of other ways of eating flowers, if you want. (As I write, a familiar roe deer in the garden is idly selecting the flowers — and only the flowers — on a rosebush, and from buttercups, phlox and, oddly, iceplants . . .)

Fresh lemonade is an unbeatable drink, but its only role in a cottage industry is as instant refreshment in your country restaurant along with the equally delicious *elderflower squash* and homemade *barley water*. You can think of many other unusual thirst quenchers, no doubt. And then there are the milk-based drinks: *hazelnut milk* (ground nuts, milk and honey, blended and served chilled — chocabloc with protein), old-fashioned *verder* (grate orange and lemon rind, mix with sugar, steep in brandy or rum for 24 hours, squeeze the citrus fruit to moisten some sugar, add water and boiling milk and the steeped peel and spirits, mix thoroughly and strain — bottle and cork immediately) or my personal favourite, *eggnog* (it must be the nutmeg) which is now sold by the carton in American supermarkets. And that reminds me of another childhood taste — *root beer*, which is not alcoholic and smacks slightly of bubblegum. It has recently become available in this country. I wonder how you make it?

Meat and fish

To be different, smoke and cure your own produce to your own recipes, especially if your livestock enterprises embrace outdoor pigs of traditional breeds, a steady supply of goat kids for meat, rare-breed sheep (the more primitive breeds can taste quite different), domesticated or wild rabbits, or prime beef guaranteed untainted by the drugs and diseases of our time and properly hung.

Curing

One automatically thinks of ham and bacon, but you can also produce mutton or goat 'ham'. Traditional recipes for *pig ham* date from the days when cottage pigs were not only home-reared but home-killed, never knowing the panic of the abattoir. Butcher the carcase properly, then sprinkle the meat liberally with salt and let it drain on a sloping board for 24 hours to 'empty the blood vessels'. Wipe it clean and rub it thoroughly with a mixture of salt and salt-petre. Put it rind-side downwards in the pickling bath and spread sugar on top; leave for three days and then pour on the vinegar. Bathe the meat with this pickle several times a day, turning it every other day. Allow 10–14 days for bacon, or twice as long for ham. Note that the bath should be wood or enamel but not galvanised metal.

Mutton ham was never highly rated but you might be able to improve on this old method. Put a leg of mutton into a pickle made by boiling three gallons of soft water with a pound of coarse sugar, two ounces of saltpetre and three pounds of common salt. Remove scum and let the liquid become cold before submerging the meat. Leave it submerged (use a weight if necessary to keep it down) for two or three months. A better method is to hang the raw leg first for a couple of days and then rub it thoroughly with a mixture of half a pound of bay salt, two ounces of saltpetre, half a pound of common salt and half a pound of coarse brown sugar, all pounded together and made quite hot over a fire. Turn the meat daily for four days and then add another two ounces of common salt. Leave it lying in the brine for twelve days, turning and basting it daily, then take it out, dry it and hang it in wood smoke for a week.

Smoking

For home use, devise a simple smoking barrel: find a large barrel without ends and set it on a sheet of iron over two rows of bricks with openings at either side so that the smoke can rise through the barrel. Cover the top of the barrel with damp sacking so that the smoke only escapes slowly; regulate the draught by adjusting the sack. Hang the meat or fish on rods resting across the top under the sacking. Start a small fire under the sheet iron, and smother it with hardwood sawdust so that it burns very slowly. The ideal temperature of the smoke is between 21 and 32°C for meat but less than 21°C for fish. The process might take anything up to three days.

For *kippers*, split and gut fresh herrings and open them out flat, then rub with a mixture of Jamaican pepper and salt, leaving them for 24 hours. Drain and wipe, put them over a rod in pairs and smoke them. The more fully the raw fish or meat is cured before smoking (for example, salt and brown sugar rubbed in), the longer it will keep.

The dairy

Dairy produce, processed under the most immaculately hygienic conditions and imaginatively marketed, gives plenty of scope for cottagers, especially with the increasing distrust of commercial herds and dairies. People worry about BSE (the disease), BST (the milk-boosting hormone), listeria, antibiotic residues, allergies to cow's milk, and heaven knows what else. It must be remembered that milk is a living substance and bacteria can play havoc or can be properly harnessed to help make preserves like cheese and yogurt. You must have very high standards indeed if you are dealing with dairy produce.

There is an increasing demand for milk from animals managed 'organically', untainted by disease or by the pharma-ceutical prophylactics used to combat disease because the scale of the system has outrun the ability to regard animals as individuals and to practise good old-fashioned husbandry. There is also an unsatisfied demand for the milk of goats and sheep but only where hygiene is scrupulous and the supply constant. The problems are to locate the market, to exploit it and to produce enough, regularly, to meet the demand you have located. Again, it is the marketing that so often pulls the rug out from under the feet of innocent cottage dairy dreamers more than the techniques of dairy production, especially when those feet are already entangled in bureaucratic red tape.

Take care that the breed you choose as the basis of a dairy venture is appropriate not only for ease of management or productivity but also for the quality of the milk. Does your venture need the rich butter-making cream of Jersey and Guernsey cows (it is easier to separate out the cream because the fat globules are larger) or the cheesemaking qualities of Red Poll or Gloucester cows or are you seeking quantity rather than quality from a Holstein? Is your breed of sheep suitable for milking anyway or is it a decidedly get-your-hands-off-me Soay rather than a purpose-bred, parlour-happy British Milksheep or Friesland? Most of the goat breeds in Britain are in fact highly specialised dairy breeds, and generally amenable, but here it is a case of the individual: occasionally you come across nannies whose milk is invariably slightly tainted, and often the trait is passed to their daughters as well.

Everything connected with dairywork must be very clean indeed — the milkpail, the pans, jars and other containers, the implements, your own hands and clothes, the animal's udder and above all the milk itself. Do not use the family kitchen: have a separate dairy, preferably in a separate building, with a big, low-level sink, hot and cold running water, plenty of work surfaces (and all of them easy to clean), a fridge and freezer, a cooker for cheese-making and pasteurising, and masses of storage space. The floors and walls of the dairy should be tiled, and the tiles should be neither crazed nor cracked. All equipment should be sterilised before use, every time. The dairy should, as far as possible, be maintained at a constant temperature of about 70°F/21°C for cheese-making and about 50–60°F/10–16°C for making butter and storing cheese. It is best to have a different room for cheese work, to avoid tainting milk in the dairy (milk all too readily absorbs tastes and odours) and, in any case, cheese needs its special bacteria.

There is as much art as science in dairy-work and you are strongly advised to read some of the specialist books mentioned in the Bibliography — only the absolute basics are given here.

Cream

Cream can be separated from the milk by allowing it to stand and rise so that it can be skimmed off, or by using centrifugal force in a mechanical separator, which is almost essential with goat's milk as it is effectively homogenised and loath to rise. To make *clotted cream* (cow's or goat's milk) stand fresh milk in a pan in a cool place for 24 hours and then transfer the whole panful, very gently, without remixing the risen cream, to a low heat on the stove and let it warm up very gradually until the cream on the surface crinkles. Equally gently, transfer the whole pan back to a cool place for a day or two before skimming and potting the cream.

Ice-cream

Ice-cream offers scope for producing original flavours and that is what makes it an interesting venture for those who have access to plenty of raw materials. But to make ice-cream on anything more than a domestic scale you need to invest in some rather expensive equipment. This is not a hobby but serious commerce.

Butter

Butter is easier to make in summer — and that also applies to cheese, especially soft cheese, for several reasons. For a start, the dairy needs to be warm for the sake of the butter, as well as for the buttermaker.

You will need up to 3 gallons of whole milk to make a pound of butter (10–15 litres for 450g), depending on the fat content of the milk. Butter is concentrated cream: the aim in churning is to save the fat and remove as much liquid as possible. Small amounts can be made with an electric kitchen mixer but otherwise you need a churn, the choice in which is wide. Some are very beautiful and very expensive but efficient; others are more workmanlike, with the emphasis on work. First, separate the cream from the milk. Fresh cream from a separator makes milder, firmer butter but ripened cream which has been stood at 58–62°F for skimming is easier to churn. 62°F is said to be the ideal churning temperature for the cream.

Churn the cream until the butter 'comes', which it will refuse to do unless the ambient temperature is right, the milk is in the mood, and the animal has not eaten certain plants which interfere with the whole process. The butter has come when you see small yellow grains sloshing around. Draw off the buttermilk, wash the grains, strain and repeat the washing several times until the water runs completely clear. Drain off as much as possible and then work the butter to drive out all the remaining liquid: the more successfully you do so, the longer the butter will keep. Put it on a sloping wooden board and use your bare hands or wooden Scotch hands (ribbed paddles). Add a little salt to taste as you work. Finally, form the butter into blocks, or pats, stamp them with your handcarved butter-stamp, wrap in greaseproof paper and refrigerate.

Starter cultures and rennet

To turn pasteurised milk into cheese, you need to reintroduce its ability to sour and curdle by adding a starter culture. Raw milk should be able to curdle without such help. You need a different type of starter culture to make yogurt: it requires a different set of bacteria.

Rennet is a natural enzyme in a young ruminant's stomach which helps it to digest milk by curdling it. Buy dairy rennet (you can buy vegetarian substitutes if you prefer) or in an emergency use junket, lemon juice, vinegar, cream of tartar or even globe artichoke leaves to curdle the milk.

Yogurt

There are many variations and refinements in yogurt-making but the basic process involves gently heating the milk (creamy or skimmed) to 180°F/82°C and then cooling it rapidly to 115°F/46°C. Add yogurt starter (live yogurt or a culture) and mix it in well. Transfer the milk gently to the pots and put them in a well insulated incubation box to keep warm for three or four hours. Remove them as soon as you see that the yogurt has curdled and transfer to a fridge for 10–12 hours before adding any flavouring or bits of fruit etc.

Soft cheese

Raw (unpasteurised) milk produces lactic cheese: natural bacteria sour the milk for you, whether it is cream, whole milk or skimmed milk. Natural 'clabber' is raw milk which has soured of its own accord but not gone bad, and has been strained through sterilised (boiled) muslin. You can simply drain the curds of whey, or chop them up and heat them gently for a firmer cheese, or press them. Add whatever flavours and textures you fancy — herbs, nuts, fruit, ale, wine, pepper, garlic . . .

You can also make renneted soft cheeses: heat milk to 165°F/75°C, cool to 90°F/32°C, stir in your starter, cover, and leave in a warm place until curds form. Drip through muslin for several hours to drain off the whey; re-mix the curds in the bag and drain again, repeating the process once or twice in 24–36 hours until you have the texture you want.

For cream cheese, heat cream rather than whole milk to 175°F/80°C and cool to 80°F/27°C. Stir in the starter, cover and leave in a warm place for 8–12 hours until the curd is firm. Salt to taste (and to make it last longer) and drain in a muslin bag.

Hard cheese

Hard cheese lasts many times longer than soft cheese and is a lot more complicated to make. You also need more equipment, including cheese presses, and plenty of undisturbed storage space where the cheese can ripen over several weeks or months. Very briefly, the main stages begin rather like soft cheese: heat and cool the milk then add starter, and later add rennet. Check the curds for texture (here begins the art part!) and cut them into cubes when they are firm enough for your needs. There is a special knack to curd-cutting: start with parallel vertical cuts right through, then across at right angles to form columns, and finally use a curd knife to slice the columns into cubes. Scald the cubes, gently mixing them as you do so, then let them settle before running off the whey rather as you did for soft cheese. Break up the firm curds into marbles, add salt, and press them into a prepared mould, wrapped in muslin. Begin the pressing process under weights, gradually, taking the cheese out of the mould at certain intervals to bathe it in hot water and turn it between increasingly heavy pressings.

Unusual cheeses

In sub-Saharan Africa, milk products are valued locally but milk is usually drunk (fresh or sour) with little attempt to store or sell surpluses as converted dairy produce — mainly because of a lack of collection, distribution and marketing structures. However, lots of local experiments are in hand. ILCA (the International Live-stock Centre for Africa), for example, is

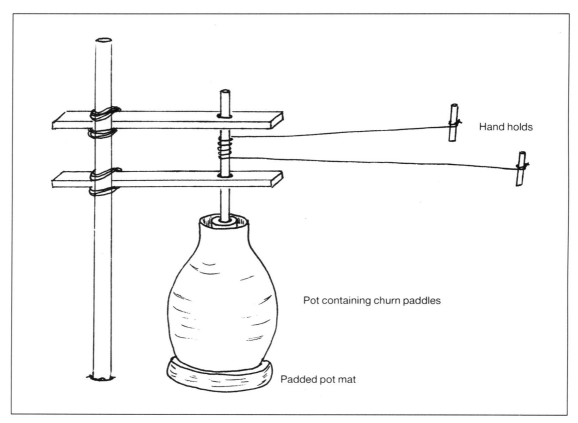

Hand holds

Pot containing churn paddles

Padded pot mat

BUTTER-CHURNING LATHE

Simple system devised for use on small-holdings in sub-Saharan Africa. The detachable agitator (a set of paddles within the pot) is driven on its spindle by the action of the hand-pulled strings wound round it: the operator uses a sawing motion. Other ingenious ideas in different countries at different times include harnessing wind-power or dogs running on tilted paddlewheels.

developing a simple detachable agitator for churning: it is very much a wood-and-string affair working on the lathe principle but effective for small-farm production and slightly more sophisticated than the traditional method of churning soured whole milk in round-based clay pots by rocking them incessantly on a mat or suspending a bottle gourd on a tripod and swinging it back and forth — a peaceful but monotonous occupation.

In Africa milk is used from several sources — cows, sheep, goats and camels — and cow's milk is the most widely produced. (Zebu cattle produce a much creamier milk than our own humpless breeds.) Fresh milk in hot climates lasts no longer than five hours, and cream perhaps a day, but fermented products have much longer lives. *Irgo* (sour milk, naturally fermented), *kefir* and yogurt can last ten days; cottage cheese only five days, spiced butter two months and ghee or butter oil (dry butterfat, i.e. with the moisture removed by boiling) more than three months.

Typical cheeses which are or could be made in parts of Africa and other tropical areas include halloumi, queso blanco, feta, domiati and gibbneh beda. *Halloumi* was originally made in Cyprus from sheep or goat's milk, heated to pasteurise (70–80°C), sprinkled with dried leaves of *Mentha viridis* and folded; it is eaten fresh or salted in whey brine. *Anari* is a cheese made from the residual whey.

Queso blanco is a Latin American cheese made by the acid precipitation of milk solids at 83°C — lemon juice can be used as the acidulant. *Feta*, originally made in Greece from sheep's milk, is a pickled cheese with large quantities of salt as a preservative — wash out some of the salt just before eating. *Domiati* is a typical Egyptian cheese (*gibbneh beda* is the Sudanese variant) which again is heavily salted.

Yemeni cheese, often called *Ta'izz*, stands on its own. To make it, you need the abomasum stomach of a suckling lamb, kid or calf aged 1–3 weeks old (to coagulate the milk). Dry the abomasum until you need it, then dip it in water and then in the milk,

squeezing it to release the enzymes. (Dry it again and for store future use.) Or squeeze the milky fluid from a fresh abomasum into a storage vessel and use a few drops as coagulant. Put the day's milk (traditionally from sheep and goats in mixed flocks) into an earthen pot, coagulate it and leave overnight to firm up. In the morning, transfer to small baskets made of datepalm leaves and allow to drain during the day. In the evening, smoke the cheese for 15–20 minutes to give it a hard, dark brown rind and characteristic aroma and flavour. Present it in round, flat cakes. Experts burn various different plants during the smoking to obtain special flavours.

They also smoke cheeses in Czechoslovakia, over pungent wood fires. Trees had a different part to play in Wensleydale cheese: its traditional flavour came from the cows' 'first bite' of fresh vegetation in spring, which included alder buds. The idea of flavouring your dairy produce by means of your animals' diet is quite appealing.

Pliny mentions cheeses soaked in vinegar and thyme. The previously mentioned directory of British country foods and the farmhouse cheesemakers directory published by the Milk Marketing Board have many other ideas for unusual cheeses.

Garden beasts

No, not tigers in the fruit cage, but invertebrates — honey bees, butterflies, worms and suchlike.

Bees

The value of bees to cottagers is renowned. Not only do they offer tangible produce but also they assist in pollinating crops, especially in the orchard. If you have a liking for bees (which is essential) and an area where they can find ample forage, then you have the opportunity to produce honey, mead, beeswax, royal jelly, propolis — but you already know all that. Once again, the problem lies in the marketing: you cannot guarantee levels of honey production, for a start. Honey can be sold as honey or converted into mead, or become an important ingredient in various remedies and culinary dishes. Beeswax (if you can spare it) is the basis of all good furniture polishes and can also contribute to cosmetics and candles — but make them special and present them well. Royal jelly can be wrapped up in pink and given a tradename like Barbara . . .

Butterflies and moths

Butterflies are quite easy to rear if you have patience and knowledge. They are ideal subjects for those seriously interested in conservation but it is essential to remember that there is little point in breeding endangered species unless you can ensure that their habitat requirements can be met. The Large Blue is a classic example of an insect whose finely balanced environment vanished, and the present attempts to re-stock in this country depend more on finding and protecting the unique combination of environmental features it requires (wild thyme and ants are crucial) than on actually breeding new generations.

As a cottage industry, butterfly farming is strictly for the specialists, though you might enjoy supplying gardeners not only with butterflies but also appropriate feed-plants for them and for their caterpillars — violets for fritillaries, for example, or birdsfoot trefoil for wood whites, lady's smock for orange tips, honeysuckle for white admirals and alder buckthorn for brimstones. Provide your customers with good literature explaining the butterfly's needs so that your breeding efforts are not wasted. Butterflies, flowers and sunshine go naturally together, both in romantic imagination and in reality. And, realistically, you could use the romance of butterflies to spread some important conservation messages which, if heeded, could have quite a radical effect on the landscape.

Moths, too, can play a part but, as with butterflies, remember that many caterpillars are quite destructive: choose your species with care. The most important moth for commercial purposes is *Bombyx mori*, the silkworm moth, whose larvae are cultivated on a huge scale in the Far East in particular to produce raw silk. It is technically possible to raise silkmoth larvae in Britain but impracticable in that you would find it difficult to obtain supplies of their staple mulberry-leaf diet (the species which grows here is unsuitable) and you could never compete in scale or price with oriental silk producers. It might be interesting to try, especially if you are involved in spinning or fibre production from more conventional sources, but be warned that you have to kill the larvae in order to harvest their cocoon silk.

Some countries farm butterflies on a large scale and then rip off their beautiful wings to supply decorative material for pictures. Don't even think of it.

Worms and compost

Earthworms are easy to breed and can be the basis of a very useful cottage industry, especially combined with compost-making. Someone has already cornered the organic market in that respect as, proudly and commercially, Lady Muck, but the demand for good compost is rapidly increasing as more gardeners turn to organic methods.

Livefood

Worms can also be farmed as angling bait, though anglers would probably prefer other 'livefood' such as mealworms and maggots. Livefood is also deliberately bred to supply cage-bird owners with not only mealworms and maggots but also crickets, locusts and various other nutritious insects, sent to mail-order customers all over the country and also appreciated by wildlife rescue centres for their hospitalised birds and other insectivores like hedgehogs. Your supplies must be reliable all year round and your delivery system infallibly fast.

Insects can also be raised as natural pest-controllers — predators on other destructive insects in greenhouse, garden, orchard and field. They include ladybirds, of course, and many parastic wasps and other species. It is a highly specialised industry and probably best left to entomologists with a very thorough understanding of the often indirect effects of releasing such predators into an environment. It's a thought to bear in mind that the locusts you are breeding as livefood for bird keepers might one day find the British climate to their liking.

Snails

Snail-farming has become popular in the last few years and is particularly suitable as a cottage industry in that you need very little space, but you do need expertise — it is not just a matter of encouraging your native garden snails by leaving stones and soggy lettuces in the veg patch. There are now one or two good sources of practical advice on snail-farming where you can find out about suitable edible species and how to market them as well as rear them.

4 Skin, Leather and Feather

Tanning and curing are different methods of treating animal skins in order to prevent them from rotting and also to keep them supple and useful. Tanning converts the skin, without its hair or wool, to durable leather; curing preserves the skin, often with the fibre intact, and leaves it supple and soft. Table 6 suggests a few cottage industries based on animal skins.

Hide is technically the adult skin of a large species (cattle and horses): it is strong and durable for harnesswork and footwear soles. *Kips* are the skins of the young of large species and are used for footwear uppers. *Skins*, in the leather trade, come from smaller livestock such as goats, sheep and pigs and are used for a wide range of purposes — shoe leather, gloves, bags, wallets, saddles, book covers, furniture and so on. *Suede* is calf, kid or cattle hide with its inner surface buffed to make the familiar nap.

Rawhide is a strong, durable material for straps and laces which can be moulded when wet and holds its shape when dry (for example, saddlebags): soak deerhide in clean water to soften it, then in a dehairing solution overnight so that the hair, flesh, fat and other gubbins can be scraped off while the hide is draped over a beam; then stretch the hide as taut as possible by lacing it to a pole frame, let it dry, release it and store in a cool place until you need it; soak in water to soften, then cut or mould as required.

Tanning

Tanning is the impregnation of the skin with tannic acid to preserve it and render it pliable, that is, to turn it into leather rather

---

TABLE 6

Animal Skins

Boots, shoes	Fur toys	Belts	Desk items
Sandals	Harness, tack	Skirts	Brush backs
Moccasins	Saddles	Elbow/knee patches	Hunting crops
Slippers	Martingales	Briefcases	Shields
Clogs	Embroidered suede or	Music cases	Tankards
Slipper-socks	sheepskin jackets	Upholstery	Barometers, clocks
Gloves	and jerkins (Polish)	Cartridge belts	Leather flowers
Mittens	Bags and cases	Ponchos	Writing boxes
Muffs	Wallets, purses	Jackets	Portraits/pictures
Sheepskin (mitts,	Pouches	Cuir bouilli armoury	Plaques
rugs, slippers,	Bottles	Parchment	Drums
coats, hats,	Laces, thongs	Domed boxes	Sculptured masks
boots, gloves)	Aprons	Camera cases	Bookbinding
Moleskin	Thornproof gaiters	Dice shakers	Bookmarks
Rabbit pelts	Jerkins	Bellows	Toys
Felt	Hats	Tabletops	DIY leathercraft kits
Fur gloves	Breeches, chaps	Desktops	Dog collars/leads

than a dry, stiff, brittle substance. The traditional raw material for the process is tannin-rich bark, especially that of oak, but today it is easier and quicker to tan leather with minerals instead, first of all pickling it in acids and then soaking it in chromium potassium sulphate (chrome and alum). Whichever method is used, however, tanning can be a messy, smelly business. Here are the basics.

Traditional bark tanning
Prepare the tanning liquor by grinding up dried bark and soaking it in cold water for a few weeks. *Clean the skin* by soaking it thoroughly in a large barrel of water for eighteen hours or so to remove every trace of blood: drape it fleshside out over a pair of broom handles with long, stout cords tied to each end and lower the skin into the water, fastening the cords to nails on the outside of the barrel. After soaking, hang it over a beam and scrape off the flesh, fat and gristle. Then *remove the hair* by draping the skin hairside out over the sticks and soaking it in a lime-pit (a weak lye of slaked lime in water) for a day, adding more lime daily for the next two or three days, until the hair begins to slip out easily when hand-rubbed. For leather intended to be tough, soak in a stronger solution for 8–10 days; for softer leather, use a weaker solution but soak it for much longer. Then put the skin flesh-side down over the beam and scrape off the loosened hairs; turn it over and 'flesh' it again, scraping off every last remnant of flesh with a sharp knife.

Now you need to *remove the lime*, either by rinsing thoroughly in clean water and using a smooth-edged slate to scrape off excess lime or by putting smaller skins into a 'bait' pit in a mixture of pigeon-loft or henhouse dung with water (or, even more effective, dog droppings and water) so that the acid solution removes the lime. Don't leave it soaking so long that the skin itself begins to dissolve: a few hours in the dog solution is long enough, and perhaps 10 hours for bird dung. An alternative lime remover is a solution of lactic acid or vinegar in water for a 24-hour soak. Then rinse very thoroughly in clean water.

Next is the business of *rounding* a hide, cutting it into specific sections to be tanned separately because the coarsest parts of the hide (belly, legs, 'cheeks' and shoulders) will be greedy for the best tannin, to the detriment of the better sections (from withers to tail, including back and sides) if it all goes in together. You might find it more convenient to split a large hide into sections before the cleaning stage, so that it is less cumbersome to handle when wet.

Now you are ready to *tan the leather*. Dilute the tanning liquor so that you can start with a very weak solution and increase it in strength by degrees during the lengthy process of tanning. Suspend the pieces of leather in the solution, none of them touching each other, for about ten days while you gradually increase the strength of the liquor. Remove them, lay them flat until all the wrinkles have gone, then re-immerse them in the pit but this time flat rather than suspended. Turn them over twice a day for the first few days and increase the strength of the solution every two or three days by adding more bark and keeping it stirred.

After perhaps 6–8 weeks, remove the pieces and lay them flat on a bed of ground bark. Cover with another layer of bark, and then another piece, and so on in a layered sandwich to build up a stack. Pour tanning liquor over the stack and leave for six weeks; then dismantle it and rebuild it with a new supply of ground bark and fresh liquor. Repeat this process every six weeks as often as necessary: it will certainly take several months and perhaps two or three years before the leather is fully tanned. Then you can wash the tanned pieces in a weak solution of the liquor, hang them over a beam to drain and use a blunt blade or smooth stone to help remove the liquor. Dry them gradually but judiciously: too slowly and they will go mouldy, too fast and they will be hard and brittle. You can give them a thin coat of linseed oil to avoid the latter problem. Start by drying them on racks in a dark, well ventilated room, then a week or so later pile them (still damp) in heaps, separated by sacking, and beat them with a wooden pin (hence, 'tan your hide'!).

Then put the whole stack on a flat surface, cover it with a protective metal sheet and run a roller over it. Hang up the individual pieces, oil them and roll them again. The tanning is complete when they are dry but that is not the end of the matter: they now need to be *curried*.

Soak the leather in water to soften it; lay it on a sloping board and scrape with a very blunt blade while pouring hot water over to scour the leather. Build up a stack again, interleaved with sacking, to let the pieces dry partially; wet again, lay them flat with grainside down, then scrape and stretch them with the aid of the blunt blade. While they are still a little damp, brush on plenty of tallow or oil and leave to dry, then scrape off any excess harder tallow from the surface.

Dye the leather if you wish: use lampblack and soap to darken the underside but on the grainside brush an overall solution of soda or urine and then brush on a mixture of ferrous sulphate and logwood. There's plenty more to this process, and you can then go on to soften the leather, beat it, roll it, water-proof it or polish it, or turn it into chamois leather.

Real oak bark is not often used in tanning today: it has been replaced by synthetics or by imported bark-tannin extracts, especially of black wattle. Some of the chemicals are dangerous pollutants and some are corrosive.

Alum tanning

For light hides, mix together 8 parts alum, 8 parts salt, 3–5 parts flour and 2–4 parts eggyolk, all by weight in proportion to 100 parts hide. Put the mixture into the pit with water and soak the hide for a couple of hours, keeping it constantly on the move. Take it out, drain it and let it dry. Simple, but hardly professional. A more detailed description of the use of alum is given for curing furred pelts later.

Chrome leather

Chrome tanning the hide of large animals for heavyduty items like harness and shoe soles is not for the amateur except for home or farm use. The first problem is that livestock have often been carelessly handled, either at the farm or at the abattoir, so that the hides are already damaged. The second problem is that the average weight of a cowhide is a good 50 pounds when it is dry, let alone wet, and it takes up a lot of vat space.

However, the chrome tanning techniques for cowhide are equally applicable to goat-skin and calfhide for lighter-weight leathers, as long as they are sound, free from disease, and without warblefly holes, careless cuts and so on.

The method involves the use of chemicals, which need to be handled with respect during the process and to be disposed of with proper care afterwards to avoid pollution. Many tanning and curing solutions are caustic and poisonous (there are several to choose from) and they should never be stored or mixed in metal containers: use wood, glass or earthenware, whether you are tanning leather or curing pelts.

Much of the chrome tanning process is similar to the bark tanning method but the timescale is greatly reduced. If you are not ready to tan the hide immediately, start by stretching the hide on the floor, fleshside up, and cover every bit of it with a good layer of salt, then rub it in by hand. Fold it flesh to flesh, roll it up, then let it drain on a sloped surface. A salted skin can be kept for several months, if necessary, before tanning.

Split the hide in sections as already described, or at least into two parts for easier handling if this does not interfere with the leather sizes you will need. Thoroughly soak it in a large barrel to clean it, with several changes of water. Flesh it over the beam, then remove the hair with the help of limewater and a good scrape; remove all traces of lime by rinsing in water, soaking in a lactic acid solution and then rinsing again.

To tan, prepare a solution of soda crystals (three and a half pounds) and salt (six pounds) in three gallons of warm water in a wooden bucket. In a separate tub, dissolve twelve pounds of chrome alum in nine gallons of cool, clear water, mixing well to dissolve the alum, then very slowly add the soda-and-salt solution to it, stirring constantly. Put four gallons of this mixture into a clean barrel and add water until it is about two-thirds full. Drape the hides over the broomsticks and lower them into the mixture, leaving them immersed for three days and moving them occasionally within it, without bunching or wrinkling them. Then add another four gallons of the solution, soak for another three days, then add the rest of the solution on the sixth day and soak a further three or four days or more. To check that tanning is complete, take a little sliver from each piece of hide and see that the edges are uniformly coloured; or boil a little piece in water — it has not had long enough if it curls up and becomes hard or rubbery. For lighter or thinner hides, reduce the proportions of the solution and reduce the time.

Now rinse the hides through several changes of water. Soak in a borax solution overnight (two pounds borax to forty gallons of water), rinse again through five or six changes of clean water and hang them up to dry.

For *heavy leather*, sprinkle with warm water until quite damp and then add plenty of neatsfoot oil on both sides. 'Slick' the hair (grain) side vigorously to smooth it out and get rid of wrinkles. Stretch it to dry on a wall or frame, then release, dampen, and oil and slick again. Then give it a thick coat of dubbin on the grainside (melt equal parts of neatsfoot oil and tallow); hang to dry; slick off excess dubbin and rub with a soft cloth to remove superficial oiliness.

For *lighter leathers*, let the drying process be slow. When still a little damp, coat the grainside with warm neatsfoot oil, stretch on wall or frame to dry out completely, take it down and dampen with warm water, then roll it up. Slick the grainside in all directions.

For *softer, more supple leather*, work it over the beam's edge and keep repeating the alternate oiling, slicking and working until it is soft enough.

Buckskin

American Indians made bucksin by soaking deer hide in water and then graining the skin over a smooth log with a crude knife to remove the hair, or soaking in weak lye. They made a tanning solution by putting the deer's brains in a loosely woven cloth bag and boiling in soft water for an hour, then cooling the water to hand-hot and rubbing the bag between their hands under the water to force the brains through the cloth. The deerskin was kneaded and stretched in this liquor for an hour, then left to soak in it for several hours. After partial drying it was stretched every which way until completely dry, then rolled up and stored for at least a fortnight before the final process: the smoking. The skin was stretched over a barrel and smoked over a slow fire of decayed wood until both sides were light yellow, then it was scoured in warm water, rinsed, dried for a week, dipped briefly in water again and worked over a stake until it was soft and pliable.

Snakeskin

Soak snakeskin for several days in a solution of three ounces of slaked lime to a gallon of warm water, then soak it thoroughly in a weak borax solution (an ounce to a gallon) to remove all traces of lime. Rinse, and put in a solution of chrome alum and salt in water, drop by drop. Keep the skin in this mixture for another week, moving it from time to time; remove, drain, soak overnight in one part sulphonated neatsfoot oil to three of water. Remove, drain, tack on a board or frame to dry then work over a beam until pliable.

Curing pelts

Rabbit farming is an increasingly popular enterprise for smallholders, whether for meat or Angora rabbits for fibre. The pelts of meat rabbits can be prepared for making fur coats and the offcuts can be made into soft toys.

If you want to use the pelt, choose the time of killing a meat rabbit carefully. Summer coats, for example, are too light-weight, and you also need to avoid periods of moult. Catch the time when the adult coat is mature and homogeneous in winter so that there is no risk of patchy moulting. The best skins can be dressed as fur-bearing pelts; others can often have the hair shorn from them for use in felt-making or spinning, while the skin itself is cut into strips to make glue or fertiliser.

Practise the curing techniques first with a wild rabbit's pelt. To skin the rabbit, chop off the feet and then make a skindeep slit from one back heel to the other, via the tail root; cut around the vent then draw the skin off the back legs and tail. Hang the carcase upside down by its legs and continue to peel off the skin carefully until you reach the front legs. Slit them on the underside from foot to shoulder. Or simply start with a belly slit after chopping off the four feet and head, then peel off the skin like a pullover, inside out. Let the pelt dry on a board or frame in a cool, airy place — not in the sun or near a source of heat. If you are selling pelts (for example to a furrier) check exactly how they want the animals skinned and presented: usually you simply stretch the pelt to its natural shape and let it dry without any form of curing, but do scrape off any fat.

The most basic way of preserving a rabbitskin intact with fur is by drenching the flesh side with borax or salt (after you have scraped off any gubbins) but it will not last long and it will not be supple. Another way is to boil together a pound of soft soap, two and a half pounds of whiting and a pint of water; stir in two ounces of powdered chloride of lime and allow to cool. When it is nearly cold, add one ounce of tincture of musk and dress the skin with the mixture, tacking it flat on a board, then let it dry. You still need to treat it further to make it soft and flexible by working it over a beam. If the soaking is in borax or soda (an ounce to a gallon of warm *soft* water) the skin softens enough to make fleshing easier, but don't soak so long that the hair is loosened. Fleshing, as with leather, involves putting the skin fleshside up over a beam so that you can scrape off unwanted flesh, fat, sinews and tissues with a blunt blade.

A small pelt can be tanned cheaply in a solution of oxalic acid, which is poisonous.

The normal method for tanning a furred skin, however, is with alum, soda and salt solutions. Dissolve a pound of alum in a gallon of water and, separately, dissolve four ounces of washing soda and twice as much common salt in another half-gallon of water. Then very slowly pour the soda-and-salt solution into the alum solution, stirring briskly. Immerse the clean, fleshed pelt in the combined solution for 2–5 days, occasionally moving it about in the liquid. Take it out, rinse in a solution of borax and water (an ounce to the gallon) and then in clear water until it is clean, changing the water frequently. Squeeze out most of the water; stretch the pelt on a flat surface, fleshside up, and tack in place. Use a cloth or sponge to apply a thin soap paste all over the skin and let it be absorbed, then apply a thin coat of neatsfoot oil. Leave until almost dry. While still slightly damp, work over a beam. The more you work it, the more pliable it will be. Finally, use warm sawdust and petrol or naphtha to clean the fur, then beat, comb and brush it out.

Moleskin

Even for a pair of gloves you need at least a dozen moleskins and probably a score. They should be cured like rabbitskins and worked to make them supple, rubbing in some lanolin on the flesh side as you flex them firmly but gently but don't let the grease go on the fur. Clean the fur with oatmeal or hardwood sawdust.

Taxidermy

Yes, this is certainly a possible cottage industry if you have a shed well away from the house — it can be very messy indeed. Borax is commonly used as the preservative. Moulding materials for bodywork include papiermâché, modelling clay and plaster of Paris; stuffings include excelsior (woodwool, hemp, sisal etc.) and a special kind of foam which expands to fill an available space. You also need wires, threads, glass eyes, surgical needles, glover's needles, skin scrapers, sharp knives and various household implements like tweezers, scissors and files, but also a set of modelling tools, ideally of boxwood, and plenty of plastic buckets. You can buy pre-formed body frames or make your own from the original animal's bones or from balsawood, cork, plastic, wire etc.

The techniques are quite complicated and are described in one or two good books, or you might be able to find a course on the subject if you cannot find a good taxidermist willing to share expertise. It is a three-dimensional art and takes a considerable amount of patience and practice.

Parchment

The initial stages of parchment-making are similar to those for leather: parchment is made from animal skin, whereas paper is made from plant fibre. Use goat, pig, sheep, lamb or calf skin and remove all traces of wool or hair from it, soaking in a slaked lime solution for a few days. Stretch the skin by lacing it to a frame and carefully use a strickle (short, broad, rounded knife) to scrape off all traces of fat and loose tissue on the flesh side, with the help of hot dowses of soda lye after each scraping session. Work to achieve a smooth surface with the help of an abrasive such as powdered chalk, fine sand, powdered pumice or limestone powder. Both surfaces should be perfectly smooth. Now split the skin into thinner layers according to requirements, stretching each layer after splitting so that you can again scrape and abrade it to smoothness. Finally, leave the parchment to dry, stretched on its frame.

Cut from the skin according to your parchment needs. The original 'folio' size was a rectangular section cut from the central panel of a single sheepskin (folded in half), whereas quarto was the folio piece halved, and octavo was half a quarto, all the cuts being across the skin rather than along its length. Thus quarto size was a skin folded in four, and octavo folded in eight. The rest of the parchment hide was used for bookbinding, or to make waterproof bags or jar covers.

Harness and saddlery

Originally, saddlers took their material right from fresh skin to fashioned product, carrying out their own tanning until pressure of work forced them to buy hides already dressed. They also used to make their own beechwood saddle-trees and they even retted their own hemp and flax, a smelly business which made them unpopular in the village. Indeed, in due course it was decreed that all retting ponds must be well away from the village, not to mention tanning vats.

The making of leatherwork for horses was more of a village or town craft than a cottage industry: a lot of skill is required and a good range of tools. Harness-making involves much stitching, traditionally by hand with beeswaxed flax but now by machine, and is as much a decorative as a practical art once the harness has been embellished with its various buckles, chains and brasses. Saddles are effectively sculptured in leather: they are shaped to the horse's back on a wooden former or tree, padded with quilted wool and built up from several overlapping parts, all shaped to contribute to the comfort of both horse and rider. Different styles have evolved in different parts of the world for various purposes.

Harness-making for farm draught animals is a subsidiary enterprise for those who make tack for ridden horses, which are of course now many times more common in this country than working horses. As riding for pleasure and sport increases rapidly in popularity to fill people's expanding leisure time, so too does the demand for the services of good leather workers but the apprenticeship is necessarily quite a long one. Most country towns still have a saddlery, so that there should be ample opportunity for the dedicated to learn the craft. Make a start by fashioning a collar and lead for the family dog and devising headcollars for your own livestock.

Footwear

There was a time when every village had its own cobbler, who was not only a mender of shoes but also a maker of boots until the

Shoe Stitcher.

mass-production shoe factories took over the business of making footwear and gradually deprived the cobbler of all but the simplest repair work of re-soling and heeling or mending the strap of a bag. Here and there a few people are hand-making footwear as a cottage industry even now, fighting the rising tide of synthetics and trainers to produce soft moccasins, sheepskin slippers and clogs more often than stout, dewproof working boots and lace-up shoes. The problem is not only to acquire the necessary skills and tools but also to find a market and assess acceptable prices.

The simplest footwear is a foot-shaped piece of sole leather stitched to a softer upper but a proper shoe or boot is formed over a wooden last from several pieces of leather cut to precise patterns so that the shape can be built up (not unlike sculpting a saddle) using different types of leather as appropriate: strong and hardwearing on the sole, protective for the toecaps, soft and comfortable for the side panels and so on, all fitted and stitched so perfectly that they defy water penetration.

The term cordwainer, often used for shoemaker, is properly applied to one who works with goatskin leather, originally from Cordova (Cordoba) in Spain. Perhaps Britain's burgeoning goat-farming industry might consider the production of leather from meat goats? With the blessing of St Crispin of Soissons, patron saint of shoe-makers, whose day happens to fall on my own birthday as well as the anniversary of the battle of Agincourt.

If you are interested in shoe-making, start by taking an old leather shoe to pieces to see how it is built. Ideally each last is designed for an individual foot so that the leather, cut from flat pieces and dampened, can be stretched and moulded over it for a perfect fit. The uppers are moulded over wooden or fired clay lasts; the outer sole is stitched and glued in place over an iron last; the heel is built up from several layers of leather and nailed in place.

To make a long leather thong, for lacing or other purposes, cut it in a continuous spiral from a round piece.

Tooling

To create a pattern, wet the leather, put it on a firm surface and use a metal implement to press firmly on the surface in the pattern you want. Keep the leather damp as you work. The tooled impression will remain when the leather dries. Practise on odd scraps with a curved nail: bang its tip into a handle, cut off its head, bend the top and file it to a smooth point as an all-purpose leatherworking tool. Leather can be tooled, carved, stamped, stitched, studded, punched, braided, dyed . . .

Gloves

Glove-making used to be a genuine cottage industry in the villages at its peak in the 19th century, and continuing well into the 20th. It involved long hours for a few pence earned by the desperate but it enabled women to work at home with an eye on the children. The going rate at the end of the century was five shillings for a dozen pairs, with each pair taking at least three hours to stitch. They used a gloving donkey with a foot-treadle which operated a pair of brass jaws to hold the leather as it was hand-stitched with a very fine needle.

At first the frames were on loan from the leather-supplying companies but as more women became cottage industrialists the firms stopped supplying and the women had to buy the frames at ten shillings each — a week's wages for the main breadwinner in the cottage. The firm's agent collected from central points in small towns each week, when the finished gloves were exchanged for new parcels of work. Combinations of French imports and competition from other glove-making materials such as cotton, silk and wool depressed the home industry from time to time, though some of the old-fashioned donkeys were still being used in the late 1930s. Now, however, gloves are machine-stitched in factories. Can you compete? Perhaps you could concentrate on fur gloves, sheepskin mitts, muffs, or thornproof gardening gloves.

Feathers

Poultry feathers should be cleaned and left to dry overnight in a cooling oven. Carefully selected feathers and down can be used to stuff pillows and duvets; prettily coloured small feathers (cast off by wild birds as well as farmyard poultry and cagebirds) can be used for hat decorations, feather pictures and unusual wall-coverings (feathers are excellent insulation). Wing-ends from larger poultry were used in the past as makeshift brooms, while individual quills had many uses: as pens, of course, or as paint brushes, bottle-stoppers, air spigots for brewing casks, arrow and dart flights, and emergency 'teats' for bottlefed lambs and piglets.

There were feather lifeboats too. Wise sailors slept on feather-stuffed mattresses covered with linen treated with beeswax or seal fat to make it waterproof so that, in the event of a shipwreck, the mattress became a raft, buoyed up by the feathers. Far-fetched? Perhaps, but there must be ways in which the natural buoyancy of feathers can be turned to good use by humans as well as by ducks.

Fishing flies

Somewhere on the streets of Aberdeen there is a taxicab with a mobile cottage industry on the front seat next to the driver, Douglas Forbes, who hand-ties flies for fishermen. His profit is a mere 4p a fly but it's a nice idea if you combine it with, say, raising livefood bait. How good is your eyesight and how delicate your touch?

5 Fibre

In this chapter, the animal's hair or wool is shorn, combed or plucked at regular intervals from the living animal, as opposed to forming its pelt or skin after death. Fibre can also be harvested from plants, mainly as annual crops though it is possible to turn wild plants into fibre as well.

Whether the source of the fibre is animal or vegetable, many of the processing techniques are similar. The individual fibres might be allowed to remain random but matted (for example, felt and paper) or need to be organised so that they lie more or less parallel and can be twisted into threads by means of spinning; the threads might be further twisted into ropes, or woven together in various ways to make fabrics. Often the fibres are also bleached or dyed rather than being left in their natural hues. Table 7 (overleaf) suggests some of the ways of using animal and plant fibre.

Fibre production and conversion could be an excellent cottage industry, and traditionally always was: cottagers raised their own livestock and grew their own fibre crops, harvested the fibre, spun it, dyed it and turned it into the final product, either for their own use or for the market. Today you need originality and a niche to be successful in marketing homegrown fibre, whether in its raw state or converted.

Animal fibre

A major bonus in the production of fibre from your own livestock is that the animals can be productive in other ways as well, so that you do not have to rely wholly on marketing fibre. Table 8 (overleaf) suggests the types and breeds of livestock suitable for fibre production (though one or two of them are not exactly traditional in Britain) and

the type of fibre they produce. Quite apart from the obvious livestock, you can also spin the combings from long-coated dogs and cats and I've seen some beautiful, gossamer-like dog-hair shawls. Conversely, the coarse hairs from a horse's tail have many traditional uses and cow's hair was a component to bind the plaster of ancient wattle-and-daub walls. And surely the shaggy, winter-matted coats of Highland cattle can be used for *something*?

In days gone by, when sheep's wool was so important to the wealth of Britain, a great many different specialist skills were involved in the processing of the fleece. They included shepherds, sheep-washers, shearers, staplers, scourers, pickers, scribblers, dyers, carders and combers, spinners, spoolers, warpers, queelers, weavers, fullers, tuckers, burlers, shearmen, pressers and packers, and also clothiers who acted as agents, bringing wool to cottagers and taking away the spun yarn for loom production and marketing at all stages. Then there were knitters, tailors, rugmakers and many more who used yarn as their basic material. Perhaps, therefore, it is asking a lot to suggest that you might carry out all the processes yourself! Could the ideal cottage industry based on fibre be a co-operative village venture instead, with the several different processes carried out at home by different specialists? As an added source of income, welcome the tourists to watch you all at work, perhaps in a converted farmyard, and offer courses in the various skills as well as selling the finished goods. Add a group of hand-knitters and crocheters . . .

The fibre at the heart of such a village industry might be wool from sheep (naturally coloured or plant-dyed), or mohair and cashmere from goats, or Angora rabbit

TABLE 7

Fibre Ideas

Skeins of natural or plant-dyed fibre for hand-knitters
Knitted goods and crochet
Tapestry
Woven cloths and carpets
Tufted rugs
Cloaks and shawls
Blankets, picnic rugs
Horse/livestock blankets and jackets
Pet jackets
Furnishing fabrics

Church hangings
Wall hangings
Smocks, aprons, other clothes
Prints
Mohair and cashmere
Alpaca
Yak fibre
Silk
Bristle/hair brushes
Horsehair stuffing
Horsehair cloth/cord
Bowstrings

Unusual uses for pigbristle and horsehair
Uses for hair from shaggier cattle breeds
Lace
Macramé
Nets
Ropes and twine
Sails
Doormats
Sacking
Wall coverings

TABLE 8

Fibre Livestock

INTERESTING SHEEP BREEDS
Down breeds (fine, short fleeces and sheepskin)
Herdwick (coarse, strong, shades of grey)
Jacob (patched brown-and-white fleece)
Lustrous/longwools — Leicester, Lincoln, Cotswold, Wensleydale, Romney, Teeswater, Dartmoor, Devon & Cornwall (some of the longwools are bred for coloured fleeces)
Shetland (soft, fine, good range of natural colours)
Portland (almost as fine as Merino, hint of colour; red lambswool)
Coloured Welsh mountain breeds: Black Welsh Mountain, Torddu, Torwen, Baalwen
Coloured primitives and rare breeds: Castlemilk Moorit, Hebridean, Manx Loghtan, North Ronaldsay, Soay
Merino (rare in Britain, dominant in Australia — finest sheep's wool in the world)

GOATS
Mohair (long fibres, less fine than cashmere): Angora goats
Cashmere (the world's second finest animal fibre after vicuna, but short fibres and small yield): can be encouraged to develop in very small quantities in most breeds of domestic goats and especially ferals

Cashgora (intermediate fibre in Angora crossbreds)

SOUTH AMERICAN LAMOIDS
Vicuna (finest of all, but a wild species)
Guanaco (also a wild species; fleece difficult to spin)
Alpaca (stiffer and stronger than wool, finer than llama and much more valuable fibre)
Llama (lightweight fibre, mixture of hair types in fleece — 20 per cent longer coarse outer hairs with fine, short, woolly undercoat)

YAK
High-altitude central Asian species of cattle family, various colours; long, shaggy coat of hair plucked for felt, tents, ropes, textiles. A model for Highland cattle?

HORSE
Mane and tail hairs for horsehair cloth/cord, bowstrings, meshes, upholstery stuffing.

RABBIT
Angora breeds: long, fine fibre for shearing, various colours

Portland sheep.

Young Lincoln Longwool sheep.

Manx Loghtan sheep.

wool, or lamoid fibres, or combinations incorporating silk, and the industry could easily embrace fibres of vegetable origin as well. Once you have attracted visitors to the village, you can have a retail shop (which could sell other local craftwork and small-holder produce of all kinds) and gradually extend the concept of a productive village to include some of the other industries in this book. The spin-offs (sorry!) for the whole community could be considerable. However, you do need a central 'product' — a type of cloth or knitting, for example — to which the village can give its name and become associated with, as Witney is to blankets, Harris to tweed and Arran and the Fair Isle of the Shetlands to knitting.

I find the idea very exciting. As a cottager myself, I know how vital it is to keep a village alive through work and this could be a very good way of doing it. Look around: you will find in your own community all sorts of unsung creators waiting to be recognised and encouraged.

Managing the livestock

Britain used to produce the best wool in the world, and indeed England as a nation grew rich from wool, but the days of the golden fleece have long since gone from these islands: Australia saw the potential of the Spanish Merino and left British sheep good mainly for mutton. Wool in this country has become a byproduct of the lamb industry.

Smallholders actually have an advantage in fibre production if they are prepared to consider added-value techniques but to do so seriously you must start at the beginning: choose your species, and choose your breed within that species, then manage your animals

Angora goat. *(Photo Anna Oakford)*

and general environment. For example, cashmere and often sheep's wool tend to be finer in colder climates. You also need to take into account their age, sex, general health and temperament. Good management is especially important with an expensive animal like an Angora goat or a nervous one like the Angora rabbit (which quite readily dies of shock) or exotic species like the lamoids, which have only recently been farmed on a serious commercial basis in Britain and which have special requirements, including humans trained to understand lamoid body language.

One factor often overlooked is the need for consistency of management. With sheep, for example, a period of overtight grazing will show up in the fleece as a marked weak point in the fibre, which could even break at that point. Managing for fibre production can be more complicated than managing for meat. Different types of wool have different uses and a breeder should pay close attention

Angora rabbit. *(Photo Anna Oakford)*

specifically for good fibre production. Read everything that Dr Michael Ryder has ever written about how animal fibre grows (and he has written a lot). Learn ceaselessly about really good animal husbandry, too, including breeding. As well as breeding for good fibre production, experiment by crossing different breeds to produce interesting fleeces.

Certain aspects of fibre growth are heavily influenced by genetics, others by environmental factors. For example, the length of wool staple is largely inherited but the diameter of individual fibres is partly genetic and partly environmental. You need to look at the ancestry of your animals, and to breed them deliberately to improve fibre production, as well as managing their feeding to the qualities of the end product: even if you are selling fleeces to the Wool Marketing Board, good breeding should not stop at the field gate. This is the true bonus of the cottage industries served by this book: you see your produce right through from the raw material to the finished object at point of sale and can therefore understand exactly how your husbandry should be affected by the market for that final product, be it a knitted jumper, a cashmere shawl or a Persian carpet.

The main features of animal fibres are the length of the staple, the density or number of fibres per unit area of skin, the diameter of the fibres and the weight of useful fibre, which is a combination of length, density, diameter and general quality. Quality and quantity are not necessarily compatible. In addition you need to consider natural colour (the breeding of white-fleeced sheep was a major revolution: primitive breeds are coloured and their fleeces therefore difficult to dye in other colours, though for cottage industries these natural colours are now highly desirable) and cleanness of the fibre from field rubbish like hay, brambles, seeds and dung.

Harvesting fibre

Sheep's wool is usually shorn — carefully cut off near the skin with handshears or mechanical clippers. You can employ travelling shearing gangs but this is not advisable if fibre production is an important enterprise: some of the gangs tend to concentrate more on speed than quality. You owe it to your enterprise and to your sheep to go on a really good shearing course — not just a half-day demonstration — and to practise on a commercial flock before you shear for quality fleeces. Learn how to keep the fleece clean, how to roll it up, and how to grade it and sort the different qualities of different parts of each fleece (they are never uniform).

Some of the more primitive breeds of sheep are best hand-roo'd, if you can catch the right moment. They shed their fleeces naturally and you can simply draw or comb it out in late spring before it vanishes along the hedgerow. The fibre from Angora goats is shorn twice a year. Cashmere and cashgora can be either shorn with care or combed, and the same applies to lamoids. Angora rabbits can be clipped every three months when the fibre is about 3 in long.

In the old days, when wool was the most valued part of the sheep, it was the common practice to wash the fleece while it was still on the animal's back. Sheep-washing is not the same as sheep-dipping: the latter is to deal with parasites, though the sheep themselves might not appreciate the difference between the two processes as both involved persuading the unwilling animals to take a swim. Sheep dislike water.

Sheep-washing was often carried out by damming a stream to form a dipping pool, preferably over a gravel bed, and sometimes the washers climbed into barrels to avoid taking a dip themselves as they worked a lye solution well into the fleece. The aim was to release the dung, mud, sand, vegetable matter and other rubbish from the wool, and the opportunity was taken to dag at the same time, clipping off badly fouled breech wool. The sheep was rinsed off in a clean pool.

More sophisticated washers found ways of saving the dirty water and extracting precious lanolin from it or, more sensibly, made a point of extracting the lanolin from neck and udder wool (after shearing) by washing it first in cold water and then putting it in a cauldron, weighed down with stones or slates, and boiling it so that the grease rose to the surface and was cooled to a white fat for skimming, reheating and straining off through linen, leaving clear lanolin as the basis of a wide range of ointments, either medicinal or cosmetic. For example, lanolin impregnated with yellow broom buds was widely used to dress sheep's wounds and as a working man's hand cream.

Lanolin is a waxy skin grease, one of two glandular secretions at the wool's roots; the other is 'suint' from the sweat glands. The combination of the two secretions gives 'white' wool its natural creamy colour and is known as 'yolk', and you need yolk in the fleece to make shearing easier. So, after washing the sheep to remove all the dirt, the old shepherds would wait for a few weeks for the yolk to rise again before shearing.

The best time for shearing is just before the fleece is shed naturally. Bear in mind that shearing is likely to leave cut-ended fibres, whereas if a primitive fleece can be pulled by hand (rooing) at the time of the moult the new growth of fibres will be left intact with their tapered tips and the new fleece is more weatherproof for the sheep and generally produces a finer spun thread as well.

Learn how to prepare and spin a fleece properly and collect every scrap of information about the huge range of plants which can be used for dyeing if you are not going to use the natural range of wool colours. Hand-weavers usually dye before weaving, or even before spinning.

Then what? You could sell in the skein to home knitters, weavers and tapestry workers, or make up the wool yourself — but remember that, if you take your own time into account, handmade items must bear a price tag that might deter shoppers who are used to the prices of factory-made goods. To succeed, offer something different and identifiable — something 'branded'. Take inspiration from the marketing skills of producers of Jacob, Manx Loghtan or Herdwick wools who have made a virtue of their breed's natural fleece colours.

Spinning

Before fibres can be woven, they need to be drawn out longitudinally into threads. If fibres are then twisted together, the resulting yarn is stronger than fibres simply lying in parallel.

You can literally twist a thread by hand, with no implement other than a stick on to which the yarn is wrapped after it has been twisted, but you would do better to start with a simple hand spindle to understand the principles. Collect some hedgerow wool; get a green twig up to a foot long and cut a notch near the top to hold the yarn. Spike the end through a circular lump of potato or a holed stone, bone or piece of wood as a primitive whorl to weight the stick so that it can be twisted on a vertical axis (the weight of the whorl helps to prolong the spinning action). If the wool has been scoured (for example, before dyeing) you will need to restore some of its greasiness before spinning, in order to make the job easier and to prevent the fibres from breaking: traditional additives included tallow, butter, goose grease or vegetable oil.

Hold a handful of wool or, with larger quantities, place the bundle of wool on a stick (the distaff), supported in your belt or under one arm. Start to draw out some of the fibres with your free hand, twisting finger and thumb so that more fibres are automatically drawn from the bunch as you go. Attach the beginning of the length to your spindle and set it spinning. The length of twisted yarn will begin to grow. When the spindle has nearly reached the ground, wind the yarn around the stick and repeat. You will need to adjust the weight of the whorl according to the fineness and staple length of the wool — use a thick cardboard disc for short, fine wool.

This primitive spindle is found all over the world and is the basis of the spinning wheel: put the whorl on its side and convert it into a pulley driven by a large hand-turned wheel, with a band around the wheel and pulley. To avoid having to stop frequently to wind the spun wool on to the spindle, add a bobbin with a rotary flyer so that the yarn is wound onto it continuously, and then add a treadle to speed up the whole process and leave your hands free.

If you are a good woodworker, you can make your own beautifully crafted spinning wheels and sell them. The original simple type involves quite a lot of walking for the spinner (good exercise for the unfit): the large vertical wheel, supported on a stool, is turned by hand and you step back as you draw out the fibres from the distaff bundle; then you reverse the wheel and walk forward so that the thread is wound on to the thin rod spindle, which is connected to the wheel by a band. This type of 'great' or 'muckle' wheel is easier to make than the more sophisticated Saxony wheel, which really lends itself to creative turnery.

Spinners, always popular at rural shows.

It will probably take you an hour to spin no more than an ounce of wool at first, though you'll be a lot quicker on a wheel than on a spindle. And it will take you five hours to spin 100g of Angora rabbit fibre (you'll need 450g for a jumper). However, spinning is quite a relaxing pastime and should perhaps be regarded as such: forget about counting the minutes and costing them. You can do other things while you are spinning, especially on a spindle and whorl which you can wander around with as you spin.

Wind the spun wool into skeins, twisting the yarn into fat coils with the help of a stick through the loop at each end, then remove the stick and slip one end of the skein through the loop at the other end so that the skein will not unravel until it is needed.

Experiment by incorporating different fibres into your yarns. Angora rabbit, for example, can be spun straight but is usually mixed with silk or Merino sheep's wool, and mohair from Angora goats is often mixed with silk.

Dyeing

Start by dyeing for fun without worrying too much about the permanence of the dye. For example, a 1950s American Girl Scout handbook suggests the following campfire method. Using onion skins for light brown, spinach for green, beetroot for rose, golden-rod flowers for gold, carrots for yellow, coffee for brown and red sumac leaves for black or its berries for red, cover the chosen plant material with boiling water and let it stand overnight. Next morning, simmer the whole lot slowly without changing the water, for at least an hour. Strain off the dye water through fine muslin into a can or kettle. In the meantime, wash the yarn or material in a bucket of warm water and soap, rinse it thoroughly and wring out as much moisture as possible, then put it in a solution of clear lukewarm water and powdered alum (an ounce to the gallon) and simmer for an hour. Bring the dye liquid to the boil in its separate container; transfer the material into the dye and boil for half an hour to an hour, moving it about in the liquid to ensure that the dye reaches all parts evenly. With yarn, put the skein over two smooth sticks and keep turning it on them to spread the dye and prevent tangling. Finally, add a tablespoonful of salt to the dye solution to set the colour, boiling the whole lot for another ten minutes, then remove the material, rinse it thoroughly and let it dry in the shade.

If you are turning your fibre cottage industry into a working museum of some kind, you could employ a genuine cooper to make wooden dye tubs. The old way of dyeing was to use the biggest cauldron you could find, put the plant material at the bottom under a weighted board with holes in it (or put the stuff in a bag), fill up with water, put the washed wool into it while it was soaking wet, then boil the whole lot for as long as necessary before rinsing in cold running water and hanging up to dry.

At first the most successful country colours were greys, greens and browns and, in due course, blues, reds, yellows and black. Merchants searched their widening world for new dyestuffs like anil, and brought back seeds so that exotic dye plants could be homegrown. Before anil shrubs from India were imported to give an indigo dye, blackberries and bilberries were popular for navy blue and purple stains and in the 16th and 17th centuries berry-dyed mauve ribbons were all the rage. However, the natural colours of undyed fibres were not despised: wool ranged through creams, fawns, browns and greys to black, and unbleached linen mixed with hemp could be soft brown or russet. For country clothes, the natural

mineral red oxide turned wool a bright brick-red and was diluted with quick lime to give a pink wash for cottage walls (they also used a greenish-grey from potash and burnt sulphur). Some of the more unusual medieval colour sources, not necessarily for fabric, included bee propolis (the gum with which bees seal the hive) which gave a bright golden-yellow stain, soot for a gold shade, and a cockchafer's entrails for artist's brown bistre. Rachan, by the way, is a grey lichen which gives Harris tweed its familiar smell as well as its colour.

Some dyes can be applied straight to the fibre, in solution, and are known as substantive; others need the help of an organic or mineral mordant to attach themselves to the fibre and they are known as adjective. No mordant is needed for lichens but they dye better if soaked in dilute alkali first (ammonia or stale urine). Mordants, of which alum is typical, make the dye fast by combining with both the dye and the fibre.

Be warned that the smell in some dyeing processes can be pretty horrible, and also that the qualtiy of the water can affect the final colour. The basic steps are these:

1 Thoroughly scour the fibre clean of dirt and grease. This can be quite a chore with a fleece: use soft rainwater and soap to wash it gently but avoid matting the fibres. Rinse thoroughly. A traditional method of scouring was to soak it in a solution of urine and warm water for at least 2 hours, then rinse it in a basket in a fast-running stream.

2 Apply a mordant if required. For alum with plant dyes, use 2 parts alum by weight to 10 parts fibre and add about ½ part of cream of tartar to brighten the colour. Add the two powders to cold water in a metal bucket and heat it to dissolve them. When lukewarm (45°C/ 113°F), put the fibre into the solution and slowly bring it to the boil. Simmer for 30– 45 minutes; then remove and squeeze.

3 Prepare the dye. Use 1 or 2 parts by weight of plant matter to 1 part fibre and put the plant matter into cold, soft water. Bring to the boil and simmer until all the

colour has been extracted. Strain off the liquid and cool it.

4   Add the wet fibre to the cold dye liquid, bring gradually to the boil and simmer, stirring frequently to disperse the dye throughout the fibre. Continue simmering and stirring until the colour is darker than you want it when dry.

5   Rinse the fibre in running water and spread it out to dry.

There is, of course, much more to the art of dyeing. On the Isle of Islay, for example, Elizabeth Sykes has a thriving cottage industry creating batik designs on silk and turning them into pictures, scarves and clothes. Batik is based on waxing the parts of a design that you do not want to dye with a particular colour, ironing it off to apply to another part of the design before dyeing with a new colour, and gradually building up the design. The wax cracks willy-nilly during the process, producing an interesting element of chance in its marbling effects.

The Appendix lists some of the many sources of dyes and mordants. Somebody, somewhere, has probably dabbled with virtually every conceivable dye source but that should not deter you from making your own experiments.

Weaving

Strong, lengthwise yarns form the fixed *warp*, held taut by the loom. In and out of these are woven the horizontal *weft* yarns, very like making a basket or a wattle panel. The warp threads are stretched from a warp

Hand-made weaving loom, designed for portability as a travelling exhibition.

beam to a cloth beam, the former being wrapped around by the unwoven warps and the latter taking the woven cloth. At its simplest, the two beams are set horizontally on the ground and the warps between them are separated by pegs driven into the ground: odd warps are tied to a rod which is raised at either end on stones to lift them and allow the weaving *shuttle*, loaded with its weft yarn, to pass through the *shed* between odd and even warps. To raise the even warps for the countershed, use a flat piece of wood, then beat up each weft as the work progresses. Quite laborious.

A frame loom is a little more sophisticated. The two end beams are supported by side beams to make a frame (vertical or horizontal) and the choosen warps are raised with the help of treadles. Like spinning wheels, looms can be as simple or as complicated as you choose.

The 'in-and-out' pattern is the simplest 'homespun' weave, taking the weft over one warp and under the next *ad infinitum*. For twill, work over and under two warp threads at a time. There are endless textures and patterns which can be created by varying the number and combinations of warps raised for each course and by changing the colour or material of the warp and weft threads. Cloths of blended colours can be achieved by using different hues for warp and weft.

Start at a very simple level to understand the mechanics of weaving before trying to understand the mechanics of looms. For example, try *tube weaving* to make something like a belt. Find some firm drinking straws (or uncooked macaroni) about 4 in long. Cut some lengths of yarn about 4 in longer than the finished item will be; thread them through the tubes to form the warp. Hold the tubes in your left hand as a flat pack, with their ends aligned, and then weave in and out with the weft yarn as if you were darning. As you work, slip the woven section gently down over the tubes so that you always have a supported pan-pipe of tubes to weave over.

Simple looms for small pieces are easy to make at home. Take a light wooden box as a frame and set pins or nails into it at either end to attach the warp threads. Wind the yarn on a shuttle longer than the frame is wide. You will have to raise the appropriate threads by hand as you work and you will soon appreciate what inspired weavers to devise more sophisticated looms.

Fulling

This traditional process involves rubbing wet woven wool to make it more dense (and thus more windproof) and smoother. Originally fullers would tread the fabric with bare feet in a tub of water like treading grapes, or work it by hand on a table of long, grooved boards (12–20 ft long and 2 ft wide) laid on trestles. The cloth was soaked in warm water with soap suds and ammonia then spread on the boards and worked vigorously by hand. Then it was rinsed clean and rolled over a wooden roller, making sure that the tension was even throughout the cloth to keep its shape.

An alternative was to use a stream to power not only a carding mill (to open out the fleece and tease the fibres every which way, with teazel heads or wire teeth, so that spinning was easier) and a spinning mill but also a fulling mill or pandy to hammer the cloth, with a water-wheel powering a wooden drop-hammer.

The essence of fulling, then, is to tread or beat the wool under water in order to shrink the threads and give the cloth body. After fulling came tenting. Tall poles were erected across a field, like a fence-line, with long stakes secured to their tops. Each stake was equipped with several closely set iron hooks or tenterhooks. One selvage of the wet cloth was stretched along the topmost hooks, making sure that the tension was even, then the opposite selvage was stretched down to a lower set of hooks driven into a heavy bar which pulled the cloth down to its full width so that it could be left to dry and tighten. After it had dried, the surface was teased (with teazels) to work up a fluff, which was then shorn to an even pile.

Felt

Felt is a fabric formed without weaving. It depends on the natural ability of wool and short, fine hairs to mat themselves together and was perhaps first made by mistake during the curing of pelts. As the skins were worked in the vat, the fluff accumulated as a matted deposit and could be use as stuffing.

Hatter's felt is traditionally made from the soft underfur and shorter hairs of a rabbit's pelt, though some felters prefer wool. Felt hats became very personal items: they had the pleasant habit of setting into new shapes if they had been hung up to dry when soaking wet. A simple round, brimmed sunhat style in felt would droop into a lopsided new hat of character if flung on an upright stick or a wall-peg to dry, or would sag into a cloche if its resting place was a shepherd's crook, and it was easy to tie the brim up and down here and there in true bushman style. This characteristic tractability under tension as wet felt dries can be used to good advantage if you want to make interesting hats, which is much more exciting than making felt toys.

Horsehair

In the days when horses were essential to the economy and were numerous on the road and in the fields, hauling long-distance loads and coaches or working the land, horsehair from tails and manes was a useful, versatile and widely used fibre. It was stuffed into mattresses and upholstery; it was stretched along bows to resonate stringed musical instruments; it bound the ends of archery bows, bound feathers to arrows and made the crossed-hair sights of crossbows; it snared small birds raiding fruit trees; it was fashioned into sieves and strainer mats; it was woven into cord and cloth.

Horsehair padding

The secret of converting horsehair into a comfortable, resilient stuffing for mattresses, chairs and saddles is to curl it. The method is very specific and has much in common with rope-making in that the hairs are twisted together with the help of a throwcock or spindle such as that used in making straw ropes. The hairs are twisted so tightly that the cord seems to have a life of its own, then the two ends of the cord are brought together and it is allowed to twist itself into a double cord, just like the long lead of an electric garden mower twisting itself into a tangle. Repeat the doubling and self-twisting three more times so that you have a thick, short wad of coiled hair packed with trapped energy. Boil the wad in a vat of copperas to dye it uniformly black, and subject it to heat under pressure until it is absolutely dry. Then slice it across in short sections to release the tightly curled hairs. It makes a springy, light padding and once had a more frivolous role in padding fashionable clothes.

Hair sieves

Horsehair sieves, or tamises (tammy cloths), were used for straining preserves in the kitchen. They were made of long, white tail hairs stretched and sewn over parchment and gripped between steam-formed hoops of bent wood. Woven hair mats were used for straining cider.

Haircloth

Haircloth is woven from individual hairs: they are not first of all spun into yarn. Thus the width of the cloth tends to be limited by the length of the hairs. The shuttle is filled with a fresh hair for each pass and the cloth is woven damp, then hot-pressed and glazed. Typically it is seen as a plain black fabric on old chairs, or sometimes as a coloured damask pattern. Horsehair weaving was still a cottage industry in the 18th century, when variable lengths of glossy hairs were woven across a linen warp to make strong, resilient, patterned fabrics to cover carriage seats. Haircord was often made by plaiting the hairs as if they were straws.

Vegetable fibre

The principle of organising fibres to be more or less parallel and twisted together into threads applies to plant material as well as to animal hair and wool. In a more environmentally conscious age, it could be that synthetic materials will increasingly be rejected in favour of natural plant-fibre materials like cotton and linen.

Some of the suitable plants which used to form the basis of major industries in this contry were homegrown — mainly flax and hemp — while others, like cotton and coconut fibre, were imported. Cotton, linen and silk were the raw materials of lace-making, one of the most widespread of the cottage industries, and even today quite a few experts handmake lace and find a market for it, while many more make lace for pleasure. It becomes an addiction.

Lace

Lace-making is a technique of twisting, looping and knotting fine threads into carefully designed patterns to make an ornamental fabric, usually as a decorative finish or edging or panel. Although cotton, linen and silk are the most common fibres, you can in fact use threads of any material if they are fine enough. You need nimble fingers, good eyesight and a great deal of patience: progress is measured in parts of an inch per hour. There are many traditional lace types and patterns, often associated with a particular village, town, county or country.

The basic equipment is fairly simple. You need a lace-pillow for your lap, stuffed with straw or hay around a circle of hardboard and covered with calico, with a removable outer cover as well. On top of the pillow, pin a square of coloured felt under a pricked parchment or card pattern. Protect the work from becoming soiled by covering it with a couple of working cloths.

The most attractive implements in lace-making are the bobbins, which can be as plain or fancy as you like. The fanciness is in fact practical: if there are lots of different colours and patterns, it is easier to see which is which as you work the pattern. You will need bobbins in quantity, made from wooden dowelling (carved prettily, perhaps) or from more interesting materials like bone and ivory. Wind the threads on to the bobbins in pairs and, as a beginner, use crochet cotton while you save up for best linen and silk.

You need lots of lace pins and a good pincushion. The pins are of various thicknesses and are usually made of brass. Then you need lessons in lace-making so that you can learn the basic stitches and techniques and how not to get your bobbins into a tangle. Lace can also be made by tatting, for which you only need a special shuttle, a crochet hook, some pins and threads of cotton or linen.

Flax

Flax is the fibre from *Linum*, a species which also provides linseed oil and which used to be grown particularly in East Anglia and near Flemish and French settlements all over England, though now Ireland is the centre for flax production. The fibre, harvested as a separate crop from the oilseed, is used to make linen and (originally) lint. There are plenty of 'lin . . .' words: linsey is a mixed cloth of linen and wool, while linsey-woolsey is a thin, coarse, inferior type of linsey. Linoleum also takes its root from the plant (the seed oil rather than the fibre) and a linnet is a finch which feeds on flax seeds. I've no idea if Linnaeus himself had a link with *Linum*!

Lyngel is a linen thread. Flax is also called line — hence the 'lining' of a garment and the word line meaning a thread or cord and all the connotations including, finally, linen and, yes, lingerie. Flax produces a very durable fibre: linen can last a century if the crop is well grown and the fibre well prepared. It is (or was) made into bed linen, shirts, smocks, tablecloths, altar cloths, candlewick and so on, and partially charred linen was once used as tinder.

Not so long ago, flax was a very important crop indeed in this country. According to Baxter (3rd edition, 1834), 'The flax is scarcely superior to common grass except when in blossom, then it certainly presents a most beautiful appearance; yet on no other vegetable has the ingenuity of man been so extensively employed or exerted with such success. The legislature of the country has paid more attention to framing laws regarding the husbandry of flax than to any other branch of rural economy.'

Baxter continues: 'From its fibrous bark we procure the comfort of linen, and the beauty of lace; its very rags . . . are manufactured into the most exquisite of all luxuries, namely, the paper that enables distant friends to hold converse, and communicates the wisdom of the learned of every age and language. The seeds by expression yield an oil, which is extensively employed by painters. The husks of the seed which remain after the extraction of the oil, is sold for fattening cattle, under the name of oil-cake. The inferior seed not fit to crush, when properly boiled and prepared, is used for feeding cattle, and is said to be very nutritious: it is called flax-seed jelly. A light infusion of the seed (linseed tea) forms a useful diluent in diseases of the chest.' Indeed, the seeds also made a good hot poultice to reduce swollen limbs, and boiled flax seeds made a thick, milky drink for calves long before oilcake was invented. For bronchitis, lick a cake of linseed and honey. How can any smallholder not grow *Linum*?

Cultivation of flax

The best soils for flax are newly broken grassland on alluvial ground (ideally when only one crop of grain has been taken after the ground has been pasture for several years) and deep friable loams with plenty of composted vegetable matter. The seed is sown in late March or early April: drilled for an oilseed crop and broadcast more thickly for fibre. The seed 'should never be sown on the same kind of soil as that on which it grew' and the crop should not be grown on the same plot more often than twice in nine years.

The timing of the harvest is crucial: if the flax is pulled too soon the linen will be weak and soft, but left too late it will be dry, hard, coarse and of a bad colour. Nor should it be pulled when it is even slightly damp, as that will injure the 'bark'. If any part of the crop lodges before ripening (and some people used to guard against such casualties with an elaborate network of poles and stakes) it needs to be pulled immediately or kept separate from the rest of the crop as it will not be strong enough to withstand the rather brutal and messy processing operations. Otherwise, no flax should be pulled until it

is completely ripe, and each part of the field should be pulled as it ripens, patchily if necessary, during the summer. Note that it is essentially pulled, roots and all, and not cut. To pull: catch a handful of stems just below the head so that shorter stems are left standing for a separate handful. After pulling, sort the handfuls according to length and quality and put them into sheaves to dry.

If the crop is dual-purpose, being grown for seed as well as fibre, it must go through a process known as ripling or rippling to separate the seed boll from the stalk: use a special upright iron comb with close-set teeth to pull off the heads, or beat out the seed in the field with a piece of wood on a stick (like a heavy flail) and then sift it into a large sheet. If the seed is to be sown, however, it is best preserved by being dried on the stem: set the crop in stooks for a fortnight as if it was a binder-harvested grain crop and then stack it or barn it with the stems still intact until at least January before threshing or ripling.

For a fibre crop, the 'bark' needs to be loosened and separated from the stalk by retting (steeping in water). Tie the flax in bundles or small sheaves of equal size, evenly shaped and straight, and put them straight into a stream, reservoir or shallow pond of soft water. Keep the discolouring sunlight off the crop with a light covering of wheat straw, fern, rushes etc., and use stones to weight it in place and keep it submerged.

The aim of steeping is to disintegrate the stems so that the outer fibre is separated from the inner pith (the two are bound together with mucilage). After a week or so the bark will have loosened and this part of the process needs careful timing: the threads will rot if left to soak too long. Take it out sooner rather than later and immediately spread it out to dry — do not leave it in a heap as it will heat. Be warned that retting is a stinking business but the retting liquid is a useful fertiliser.

An alternative to pit steeping is dew retting, which produces a less yellow flax. Spread the flax over grassland so that it is constantly exposed to dew and rain. It will take a lot longer than steeping. Or, if you are really impatient, try steeping in hot water and soft soap, which should take only two or three hours whether the flax is green or has been dried and stacked for months (or even years).

The next stage is bleaching or grassing, 'the intention of which is to rectify any defect in the watering, and carry on the putrefactive process to that point when the fibre will separate from the bark, boon, reed or harl (as the woody part of the stem is called), with the greatest ease.' Heed well that word 'putrefactive': the smelliness continues. The best place for the bleaching process is on old grassland where the herbage does not grow to any great height, because if the site has too vigorous a growth of grass or weeds they will cover the flax and it will probably rot. Spread the flax evenly and very thinly over the ground in regular rows, preferably with no two stalks touching. Take care to keep the flax straight in its length at this and all future stages.

Unless you have been able to airdry the crop and keep it dry in sacks until the following spring or summer, complete the drying by slightly heating the flax in a drying-house or flax kiln — a brick structure about 15ft long, with an underground fire about 2ft 6in below the ground surface so that there is a gentle heat and no risk of the crop being caught by the flames. Use flax refuse as the fuel. The earlier retting will already have made the bark brittle and this warming seems to encourage an even easier parting of the bark and breaking of the woody parts of the stem during the laborious work of bruising and scutching which follow.

To bruise and scutch by hand, fix four thin boards about 15in long and 3in wide, horizontally with edges uppermost about 3in apart and 2ft 6in above the ground. Fix three similar boards by hinges at one end to a fourth in such a way that they can be raised or dropped as required, which each of these three able to drop between two of the four lower boards. Lift this moveable section; put a handful of flax across the four lower boards, then force down the three uppers on to the flax and between the lowers so that the flax is crushed and broken. Repeat, turning the stems over and over until all the woody parts are bruised and broken, then twist the handful and set it aside, putting in a fresh handful for bruising.

Scutching gets rid of the unwanted plant material, leaving only the fibrous matter which can then be heckled through metal combs to dress the fibres into long, silky, lustrous strands for spinning and weaving.

The woven linen can be bucked in lye to bleach it. Originally this was done by soaking the linen in deep barrels containing a potent lye of wood ashes and urine in rainwater, poured in from the top for several soakings. Then the linen was taken out, beaten and packed back into the barrel again so that fresh water could be poured through it before it was spread out to dry and bleach. Lime could bleach it on a commercial basis but at home the housewife relied on laundering and sunlight. In Persia it was the custom to dye linen with anil.

Similar processes can be used to make cloth from hop bines or even from potato stalks and any other fibrous plant material you can imagine, including hemp.

The pretty blue flowers of the flax field are blooming again for linseed cultivation: they surprise you because the field is suddenly blue for only a few hours during the day. Linen has recently become something of a boom industry again in Ireland, but a high-tech one rather than a cottage one. The most prized Irish linen is finished by 'wet-processing' which, in the 18th century cottage, meant boiling homespun flax in a pot on the hearth. Dew-retting has largely replaced steeping (though the latter is considered to produce the finest fibre even now) and is itself likely to be replaced by alternative forms of enzymic retting when current experiments bear fruit. White-flowered varieties are replacing the beautiful blue haze. The flax is usually bought as a standing crop just before it flowers in late May and is pulled in July by the handful, as it always has been. It is still dried, crushed and scutched to remove the woody bits, leaving the fibres intact.

Hemp

Hemp is the plant *Cannabis sativa*, a member of the mulberry family (like hops) and the same species which yields the narcotic drug and also oil-rich seeds used as birdfood by aviculturists. It used to be grown on a large scale in Britain, especially in Dorset. It is still grown in parts of Romania (ostensibly for fibre to make a linen-like fabric) where it is recognised as an excellent cleaning crop capable of smothering every kind of weed, including couch.

Hemp yields a coarse fibre and a similar material is obtained from several other plants including imported sources such as *manila* (the leaf of a tropical fibrous plantain, abaca, used for making strong paper), *sisal* (the fibrous leaf of the agave, an aloe-like amaryllid from Yucatan giving a white fibre), *sunn hemp* (the Indian *Crotalaria*, a papilionaceous genus which includes the podded American rattle-boxes) and the Australian *hempbush* (*Plagianthus*) of the mallow family. Akin to the mallows are the *Corchorus* species, members of the Tiliaceae (which includes lime trees) that grow in Pakistan and China: two of them produce the brown fibre known as *jute*, used for making mats and sacking. *Coir* is the fibre from coconut shells, mainly used for door-mats but also sometimes for rope if the latter is required to float.

Hemplike fibre is also found in, for example, the hemp nettle (*Galeopsis*) and indeed the fibre of the common stinging nettle has its uses. There is a hemp palm, too. Hemp from various sources is used extensively in rope-making: the cannabis type makes a strong, coarse rope; manila a smoother one of equal strength; while jute gives a cheaper and rather hairy rope.

English-grown hemp used to be considered much stronger than any of the imported materials. It is best grown on old meadow-land or a sandy loam with plenty of black vegetable compost. The seed is sown from mid-April to early May, broadcast, and you'll need scarecrows or rude noises to keep marauding birds away. Like flax, the hemp crop was often supported by a net-work of rods or lines to prevent lodging and,

also like flax, it was grown for seed as well as fibre, but there was a difference in the harvesting. Hemp plants can be male or female and the two ripen at different times. If only fibre is required, both male and female plants can be pulled when in flower (their perfume is said to be an aphrodisiac!), but if seed is needed as well as fibre the male plants (which do not bear seed and which blossom about a month earlier than the females) are pulled as soon as their flowers fade: their stalks are easily recognised by the yellowish cast. The female plants are pulled when their seed is ripe: the capsule turns brownish or greyish and the leaves begin to fade.

Male plants for fibre are, like flax, tied into small bundles as they are pulled and are immediately taken to the watering pools. The seed-bearing females are bundled and stooked like grain until the seed becomes firm and dry so that it sheds freely. However, to avoid any delay in watering the fibre, the seedheads can be cut off and dried separately, on canvas in an airy shed. This is indeed preferable for the sake of the hemp: when green, the seeds and pods are so glutinous that they can discolour the stems long before they are dry enough, and anyway threshing would damage the fibre.

Hemp is retted, bleached, grassed, bruised and heckled just like flax, though regional customs varied — in some places it was dried rather than grassed, and in others the female crop was not watered but was dried and stacked until the following spring, when it was dewed or bleached. On the continent they used the hot-water-and-soap technique to separate fibre from woody matter quickly rather than waiting for weeks during steeping and grassing.

Ropes

The rope-making industry was more of a town trade, or confined to fishing villages to supply the local fleet. But sometimes rope-walks were found in most unusual places. Right up to the mid-1970s ropes were being made in the entrance of Peak Cavern at Castleton, Derbyshire, as they had been for more than four centuries in what was once an extraordinary underground village: the rope-makers and their families literally built cottages in the huge cavern entrance. In the 19th century they were working night and day, making everything from hangman's ropes to clotheslines, window sashes and whiplashes, and their ropes could last forty years.

Just as straw rope served the peasant and the farmer, hemp rope served the fisherman and the sailor. A 16th-century sailing ship, for example, needed several miles of cordage and a 19th-century man o'war could use the annual output of 320 acres of hemp. The main uses were for sails and tackle (from huge ships' cables to herringboat nets); and huckaback for towels and tablecloths (stronger and warmer and ultimately whiter than Irish linen). The seeds produced oil for artists and formed part of the human diet in Russia, or were fed to poultry to increase egg production or to fancy finches — but not too much as their plumage colour might change.

To make a rope, you need space for a rope-walk, which is simply an open area (indoors or out) long enough for you to twist a good strength of rope. Some used to be 800 ft long. The standard Naval rope measured 120 fathoms.

Like spinning a fleece, rope-making is based on twisting the fibres into a long, continuous yarn. The strength of a rope comes from compounding the twist: yarns are twisted together as strands, then three strands are twisted together into a rope, and three ropes are twisted together into a cable. All that twisting produces a very, very strong length.

The principles of making a straw rope or of spinning wool serve as models for making a hemp rope. The yarn is formed with the help of a vertical wheel, about a metre across, which drives several hook-ended rollers. Wrap a handful of heckled hemp around your waist and draw out a few fibres between finger and thumb, twisting them together to start the yarn as you would with wool, then attach the free end to one of the wheel's hooks. As an assistant turns the spinning wheel, walk backwards away from it and feed out more hemp as you go, letting the turn of the wheel twist and draw them. As with straw, the thickness of the yarn is governed by a combination of the speed of the wheelspin, the rate of your backwards walk and the number of fibres you draw out. The yarns are then twisted, anticlockwise, into strands.

To 'lay' the strands into ropes, you could use a whimbrel as for a straw rope but for reasonable lengths you need at one end a post with a hook and turning handle (the traveller) and at the other a set of geared wheels driving three separate revolving hooks (the tackleboard). The single hook at one end is revolved in the opposite directions to those at the other. The strands are attached separately to the three tackle-board hooks and knotted together over the single hook of the traveller at the other end, then they are twisted together clockwise (i.e. in the opposite direction to the twist of the strand) with a hand-controlled wooden 'top' shaped like a cone with grooves to channel each separate strand, feeding them into the twisted rope to maintain its uniformity. Finally the rope must be polished — and that is a whole art in itself.

The basic system can be adjusted to make anything from garden twine to hefty ships' cables, including agricultural and equestrian ropes, barrier ropes, rose pergolas, bannisters and bell ropes. A rope-maker can also convert the lengths into simple cattle halters, woven twine halters, belts, webbing, coarse canvas and sacks (hessian is woven from jute), coir doormats, plant mats, and a wide range of nets and netting. Experiment with other rope-making materials like juniper bark or linden bark, macerated in water to separate the fibrous layers: the lime strands can be made into mats.

Nets

You could start a net-making enterprise by fiddling about with baler twine to make haybags for your stock or plaited dogleads. The principles for haybags are simple enough: knot together as many strings as you need at one end, then knot them in pairs at a short distance from the main knot, then knot one of a pair to one of the neighbouring pair and so on, keeping the knots equidistant and creating a diamond mesh. Later you can become more sophisticated, making anything from fishing nets to decorative macramé — all from crops you have grown, harvested, treated, spun, dyed and knotted yourself.

Paper

Hemp was once used in considerable quantities for making paper, and indeed many fibrous plants can be converted into paper with a little ingenuity and a lot of work. Although most paper today is made from woodpulp, you can use much faster-growing crops than trees, which means that you can re-stock much more quickly too. What you need is the plant's cellulose, which can be extracted from freshly harvested plant matter or recycled from rags of plant-based materials like cotton and linen. Experiment on a very small scale with fibrous plants like nettles, flax, rushes, cabbage stalks, potato stalks, esparto grass, bracken and cereal straw. There is a paper mulberry in the Pacific islands and there is an Asiatic tree (*Araliacae*) which produces a pitch that is sliced and flattened to make rice-paper. Papyrus, of course, was one of the earliest materials to be used as a surface for writing.

As a cottage industry, you will find paper-making far too time-consuming to be cost effective, though it would be pleasant to have handmade paper for very special use — perhaps an extremely expensive limited-edition book. The main stages are these:

1 Mix the plant matter with water and beat it firmly, for ages, into a pulp.
2 Heat the pulp in a vat, stirring constantly. Remove it with a shallow mould (wire-mesh tray or deckle) and sieve off surplus wetness through fine mesh.
3 Stack the drained pulp in layers sand-wiched between pieces of felt and press it into sheets under tremendous pressure to squeeze out the moisture.
4 Dry each sheet separately in a warm atmosphere.

You could add alum (aluminium sulphate) to size the paper after beating and before vatting, or use soap, or wait until the sheets are dry and then dip them in gelatine and starch, press again and dry again. Then you can experiment with marbling or turn your attention to printing — start simply by making block prints from everyday articles like potatoes, corks, wood, lino and erasers on which you can carve relief patterns with a pocketknife.

You could also experiment with home-made ink from blackthorn bark (described in the Woodland Byproducts section) or from oak galls boiled in water with a few cloves and ferrous sulphate.

Papiermâché

Yes, you made papiermâché trays and bowls and masks and helmets and puppets at nursery school (oh, those old newspapers and flour-and-water pastes and poster paints . . .) but in fact papiermâché was once an important medium for decorative and useful items, some of which could be quite valuable. With a knowledge of the technique, you can even make furniture.

The joy of the medium is that it can so easily be moulded to any shape, however elaborate, and it is both light and surprisingly strong. The equipment is simple and the raw materials cheap; indeed, it is an excellent way of recycling waste paper and you can turn all those weighty masses of Sunday newsprint into something useful, something pretty, or both.

There are two main techniques. The paper can be pulped so that it can be fashioned like clay or plasticine, or it can be laminated (the school technique).

Pulp
Boil the paper in a little water, beat it to a pulp, mix the pulp with glue and mould it.

Laminate
Tear old newspaper into strips perhaps a couple of inches wide. Make up some wallpaper paste in a large bowl. Prepare the shape over which the papiermâché is to be formed — perhaps a bowl, a box, a tray, a pot, a balloon — by smearing it with

vaseline so that the finished article will be easy to remove. Then simply coat both sides of each piece of paper evenly with paste and put them over the shape, building up the overlapping pieces until it is at least six layers thick, and pressing out air bubbles or bumps and wrinkles as you go. (If you use contrasting paper colours for each layer, you can see where you are.) Leave it to dry near a radiator, slip if off the mould and then paint it. Use a base of, say, emulsion or gesso, then top coats of whatever you like — acrylics, poster paint, inks and so on — and finish with a protective coat of varnish.

For a more complicated item like a doll or an animal, first make moulds for the different parts using modelling clay, plasticine or chicken-wire, then laminate them as above and, when dry, carefully use a scalpel to cut each part in half so that the two sections can be removed from the mould if its shape does not permit simply slipping off the whole piece. Glue the two parts together again with a waterproof glue, let it set and then put another layer of papiermâché over it to conceal the seams if necessary.

6　Workshop and Studio

First of all, here is a table of inspirations for creative cottage industries, ranging widely (though not comprehensively) from large enterprises that need a fully equipped workshop and several years of apprenticeship to smallscale handicrafts and lapwork. Many are beyond the scope of this book because they are not directly related to materials which are or can be produced at home (animals, plants, local minerals) though several might be deemed appropriate, or because the length of apprenticeship is considerable and you need vocation, dedication and a long-term view and will already be interested or deeply involved in the craft. Several publishers produce a wide range of leaflets and books with practical details about studio crafts — you will see

their titles listed in the catalogues of good handicraft suppliers.

The following sections consider more closely crafts using animal byproducts such as horn, bone, shell, tallow and wax, minerals such as clay and stone, and, very briefly, metalwork because it has always been so important to rural life.

Horn and bone

Horn, the forerunner of plastic, is a surprisingly versatile material. It is durable, tasteless, non-inflammable and waterproof; it can be carved or turned, polished to a handsome gloss, split or pressed into sheets fine enough to be translucent, moulded to

---

TABLE 9

Some Studio Crafts

Bottle gardens, terraria	Pyrography	Cork	Tapestry
Glass engraving	Picture-framing	Resin-casting	Cushions
Blown glass	Bookbinding	Keyrings	Rug-making
Stained glass	Calligraphy	Signwriting	Flags, bunting, hot-air balloons
Mirrors	Origami	T-shirt printing	Kites
Sculpture (various media)	Cards, posters	Screen printing	Upholstery
Sundials	Crackers	Batik	Fans
Stone-casting	Christmas decorations	Silk printing/ painting	Masks
Plaster moulding	Clocks	Tailoring/dressmaking	Puppets, toys, dolls' hospital
Slate scribing	Pewter, copper	Patchwork, quilting	Lamps, lampshades
Stone-polishing	Cloisonné	Collage, appliqué wallhangings	Narrowboats, fairgrounds
Jewellery	Enamelling	Smocking, embroidery, beadwork	Vintage cars
Alabaster, marble, onyx	Stencils Cameos Badges		

---

shape after warming, sawn with a hacksaw, honed with a file and even 'welded'.

Antlers can be mounted if that is to your taste but the cleaning process is laborious and can be messy. You can also, if you fancy, convert animal skulls into 'decorative' articles but the cleaning is even more unpleasant: the simplest answer is to submerge the skull in a pondful of fish or bury it in a compost heap and let natural scavengers do the work for you.

Bone, which is calcium rather than keratin, is nothing like as amenable but, with a little imagination, you can easily turn a length of cleaned marrowbone into a varnished or gloss-painted container (use Plastic Padding to cover one end as a base), making the most of the gentle natural shape of the bone. The family dog can no doubt help you with the cleaning of a marrowbone and the birdtable tits will soon clear out any pieces of marrow the dog's tongue failed to reach. Or thoroughly boil raw bone in a solution of lime and soda, then bleach it in the sun.

To return to the more promising material, horn, your equipment for a reasonably commercial cottage venture need be no more than electric buffers, hydraulic presses and infra-red softeners, with whatever additional tools you find necessary for cleaning, polishing, sawing, flattening, splitting, rasping, moulding and colouring. Table 10 suggests some of the many items which can be fashioned from horn.

To clean 'green' horn

Immerse the fresh horn in boiling water until you can ease out the honeycombed bony core (if there is one) and remove any bits of skin or flesh. Try using pliers to draw out the core, or screw a coachbolt into it, clamp the other end of the bolt into a vice and gradually pull. Wash the horn thoroughly in hot, soapy water or a solution of bicarbonate of soda, scrubbing it very clean (especially rough-surfaced horns like antlers) unless you wish to preserve the natural patina. For a sounding horn, all you now need to do is to fashion the mouthpiece.

To cut

Use a metalwork hacksaw to cut horn, either across to retain its ring shape for various round containers or lengthways in preparation for carving, moulding, splitting, pressing etc. If you are making a comb, the teeth are cut with a special two-bladed saw or stradda. To make a simple pair of spoons or salad servers, just saw a cow's horn in half lengthways then rasp and polish the two pieces into shape.

TABLE 10

Horncraft

Drinking horns	Fan sticks	Inlay
Powder flasks	Shoe horns	Boxes
Sounding horns	Scoops	Caskets
Grease/ointment pots	Paper knives	Keyfobs
Crook heads	Spatulas	Bobbins
Stick handles	Whistles	Skewers
Ink horns	Galleons and other models	Buttons
Beakers	Lantern panes	Handles
Pencil cups	Window panes	Shakers
Napkin rings	Jewellery	Egg cups
Circular boxes	Hairslides	Toggles
Spoons, ladles	Combs	Spice jars
Salad servers	Door plates	Hinge pivots

To polish

Use rasps and files for rough finishing and shaping, then charcoal paste, sandpaper, fine glasspaper, pumice powder, jeweller's rouge, a buffing wheel, ground wood-ash and fur or lambswool for the final polish.

To flatten

Heat the horn to make it malleable. Hold it over a naked flame but be careful not to singe it, or put it in boiling water or use an infrared heater. Slit it lengthways and carefully open it out; then, while it is soft and pliable, use sustained pressure to flatten it — heavy boots, weights, presses, rollers and so on. Leave it under pressure until it has set cold and hard. This is now hornplate.

To split

If horn is soaked in water for several weeks, its layers can be carefully separated with a special knife. If you want it for glazing a lantern (literally, lant-horn), choose a pale horn which has the potential to become translucent. Use scrapers and sandpaper, glasspaper and jeweller's rouge to fine down the split-off horn leaves. They can be made translucent enough for virtually unbreakable lantern panels or perhaps an unusual porch lamp, and were once used as windowpanes.

To mould

As with flattening, make the horn or flattened hornplate soft and plastic by boiling or heating it, then press it into a suitable mould while it is soft, clamping it in place until it has set cold, or bend it over a former.

To make containers

Flat-bottomed beakers, boxes and other containers were originally crafted so that the preciseness of the fit of the handcut base ensured that they were watertight. You would be wise to use a good epoxy-resin glue, however.

To colour

A traditional dye for horn uses an ounce of logwood chips, ¾oz copperas and a pinch of China Blue, boiled together in a pint of water and applied hot in thin coats to build up the desired colour. Fix by wiping with vinegar and rust. Or use a modern wood-dye or boot polish. Bones, after they have been smoothed with glasspaper, are easily coated with household paints and enamels.

Scrimshaw

This is said to be an Eskimo or sailor's art. Whale's teeth often form the raw material, which is engraved and the pattern is shown up by rubbing lampblack or ink into the engraving. Mention of lampblack reminds me of one of the most powerfully simple art techniques I have ever seen: in the cavernous, compartmented, whitewashed cellars of a substantial Wiltshire mansion where prisoners of war long ago had used candle-smoke to 'paint' images on the damp walls.

Eggshell

The decorating of an egg can be as simple as dyed hard-boiled eggs at Easter or as elaborate as imitation Fabergé if you first blow the egg and then use all your artistic skills. Some hand-painted eggs are gorgeous, especially if the intrinsic shape of the egg enhances the design. In some ancient cultures the egg was worshipped as much for its pleasing shape as for its encapsulation of fertility and life.

It is painstaking work: a single hen's egg can take a whole day or more to paint with acrylics, enamels, sprays, nail varnish and so on. You will probably need several coats of varnish and perhaps ballentine to strengthen the shell as well. You can make raised patterns on the surface with gesso plaster from an art shop or you can follow the Victorian passion for decorating eggs (especially ostrich eggs) with beads, literally punching them into the shell. The Slavs did the same with false wax eggs and the Czechs converted blown eggs into decorative pitchers with paper handles and necks. Eggs can be made into delicate boxes with hinged lids, or cut out as elaborate arches and cages to surround a decorative article, or converted into tulip-shaped flowers, birdnests, baskets, pendants, earrings and brooches. If the essential egg shape appeals for its own sake, you can make decorative 'eggs' from earthenware, porcelain or china (literally nest-eggs to encourage a hen to sit), wood, glass, ivory, alabaster, silver and other metals, enamelwork, ormolu, bone, plastic, cardboard, chocolate . . . You can use the egg shape with a purpose, to house sewing-kits or jewels, perhaps. For those who already have a business selling real, fresh, free-range eggs, a craft of fashioning eggs in other materials or painting hen's eggs for sale seems a natural extension to the enterprise.

Choose from hen's or bantam's eggs (the latter are usually stronger shelled), beautifully translucent duck's eggs, tiny patterned quail's eggs, huge ostrich eggs (you need a power drill to cut them), rhea's eggs (about half the size of ostrich eggs), goose eggs (most versatile of all) or expensive emu eggs, which are dark green on the surface but can be scratched through to paler green and white layers.

To blow an egg

Make a hole at each end, about the diameter of a skewer (pin holes are too small) then push a needle in to stir the contents. Now blow into one hole so that the contents emerge through the other.

To cut eggshell

Use the circular blade of a craft drill or an ordinary junior hacksaw. Use a rubber band as a guide around the circumference or a paper template for more complicated, wavy cuts.

Wax and tallow

Candles can be made by dipping, moulding or rolling. Dipping involves gradually building up the thickness of the wax or tallow around a wick (or a rush) by alternately lowering it into the melted grease and cooling it, time and again. Moulding is pouring molten material into moulds around the wick and leaving it to set. Rolling is with sheets of beeswax.

Wicks

Wicks can be of linen or cotton, woven or plaited, and should be of a thickness in proportion to the candle's diameter to ensure successful burning. If the wick is too small, it 'drowns'. Note that a twisted wick is not nearly as efficient as a plaited or woven one and will need constant trimming while it burns.

Tallow

Tallow is animal fat, from cattle, sheep or pigs, and was traditionally used in large quantities for candle-making — hence the emphasis on breeding very fat animals in the past (and hence the original demise of Bakewell's Longhorn cattle, bred for plenty of tallow). It is a smelly grease, but was always cheap. Its quality is affected by the living animal's diet: an animal fed on dry food like hay and grain produces a very hard fat, which makes candles that tend to break. When candles were essential, they were made from 'summer tallow' from animals feeding on grass or perhaps roots: it was soft enough not to crack. If it was too soft, beeswax was added to harden it.

Dips

To make traditional tallow dips, melt the tallow while you cut wicks to twice the candle length then double them, twisting them together loosely. String the wicks by their loops along a horizontal rod or wire and weight the bottoms of the wicks to keep them straight as you dip them slowly into the melted tallow in a deep container (preferably a wooden dipping box with a tin or sheet-metal base) or spoon the fat over them from a broad, shallow pan, pouring it from the top so that it runs down each wick. Only apply as much as will harden and, when it has done so, repeat the process a few times to build up the layers, carefully removing base drips at each stage. Rest the rod or wire across a supporting frame to cool. A well-made dipped candle will be cigar-shaped, with the loop of wick protruding, but a roughly made one will taper.

Moulds

The old moulds for tallow candles were made of tin (try plaster of Paris) and were slightly tapered in shape. The wicks were strung on their rod, as for dips, and inserted into the moulds plumb centre, with a knot to keep them in place while melted tallow was poured in to fill the mould. Leave hanging to cool. Tallow shrinks slightly as it cools and it is therefore easy to withdraw the candle from the mould.

Dubbin

Tallow was a traditional ingredient in dubbin for polishing stable tack: warm and stir together 50 parts by weight of tallow, 40 parts of neatsfoot oil, 9 parts of paraffin wax and 1 part of aluminium stearate. Mix well, then cool in suitable containers.

Paraffin wax

Refined paraffin wax is used with additives, especially stearin (animal or vegetable fat extracts), a flaky wax which acts as a hardener, makes release from the mould easier and dissolves dyes for coloured candles. Wax whitener can be used for opaque white or pastel shades. You can buy wax dyes; some of them are already perfumed, or you can buy separate liquid perfume for candles. Always use a double-boiler for melting paraffin or any other candle wax and make quite sure you do not heat paraffin wax above 200°F — it can be very dangerous. Moulds can be bought readymade from metal, rubber, plastic or glass, either plain or embossed and in all sorts of shapes.

Beeswax

To render beeswax, make yourself a solar wax extractor: a box painted black on the outside to absorb heat and with a glass lid like a garden frame. Inside the box put a half-cylindrical vessel (on its side) of bright sheet-metal to hold the bits of comb, with a strainer riveted or soldered to its curved lower lip and draining to a receptacle for the sun-melted wax. This wax will be pure, bright, clear and ready for use without anything other than solar energy.

In winter you would have to render the wax in a double saucepan, putting the comb in the top pan and boiling water in the bottom one. *Never* render or melt wax in a pan which is in direct contact with a source of heat: you will ruin the wax and probably the pan as well.

Beeswax candles

For beeswax dips on a small scale, tie the wicks to a skewer and put the melted wax in a tall container, then dip and cool alternately. For moulded candles, add about 10 per cent stearic acid (by volume) to clear, pure, melted beeswax heated to less than 200°F.

You can improvise homemade moulds with a length of metal pipe, or small tins and jars, or a plastic squeezy bottle emptied of washing-up liquid. Tie cotton threads across each end of the mould and fasten the wick to them so that it is held centrally.

Beeswax polish

Grate beeswax into turps to dissolve for a few days, or warm them together over boiling water in a double saucepan. In a separate pan, combine grated soap and perhaps a herbal infusion. Cool, and blend together to a cream. You could include white wax, camphor and Castile soap for a furniture cream, and a little household ammonia. (For leather furniture, a better mixture is natural oil of turpentine with boiled linseed oil, vinegar and granulated white sugar.) Incidentally, beeswax has a high melting point and is therefore a useful lubricant in situations where friction causes heat: that is one reason why it was so often used to wax threads.

Clay

If you happen to have clay on your land, do not swear at its intractability as a plant-growing medium but dig it methodically, weather it for years, work it laboriously and see if you can convert it into something useful or decorative like adobe (sunbaked building blocks), bricks (fired building blocks), tiles, drainage pipes, pottery, sculpture or smoking-pipes. If you ˙can succeed in making any of these from your own clay, you will be unusually lucky!

Building with clay

You might feel inspired to attempt building with your own bricks — perhaps an ornamental wall or a small shed for the goat as an experiment. A cottage would be quite a different challenge and hardly economical with handmade bricks. But you could have fun making livestock buildings with earth in various forms: simple rammed earth from fairly sandy soil mixed with clay, adding some coarse aggregate and perhaps a sprinkling of cement or lime, all pounded down between strong wooden shutters to hold the material in place while you ram it in from above before moving them to the next section. You can preform rough blocks of rammed earth (more clay than sand) by putting the mixture into moulds while moist, or you could try putting clay-sand mixtures between two walls of woven hazel wattle. Or you could add chopped straw or heather to sticky clay and chalk or broken slate (shilf).

All these are varieties of cob-walling (also known as clob, clom, clem etc.) and they need to be rendered to protect them from the weather as they have not been fired. A simple limewash might be adequate: mix cement and lime together well (one part to three) and make the mixture creamy with water, adding colour if you wish. A more old-fashioned method is to put a bushel of quicklime and twenty pounds of tallow in a barrel of rainwater, slake it with hot water, cover the barrel with sackcloth to keep the steam in and then let it cool before sieving and applying the sieved liquid with the help of enough water to make it creamy.

Quicklime is calcium oxide, made by heating limestone rock in big brick kilns over brushwood, or in a mud-covered clamp as if firing bricks or making charcoal. It is the sort of stuff which is used to dispose of the buried carcass of a diseased animal — watch out! Slaked lime is calcium hydroxide — a solution of quicklime in water — and it is benign but the process of slaking releases a lot of heat.

Wattle and daub was originally used in building all small houses and outbuildings and in timber-framed houses. The interstices are first filled with straw, dry moss or the short hairs from tannery lime vats, or reeds, rushes, marram grass or wool — anything to hold the clay, which is 'thrown' at the wall and pressed into it.

Bricks

Bricks, roof tiles, chimney pots, drainage pipes — hardly a cottage industry but very much a village industry. The ruined ack-houses of the local brickworks hide under the brambles in my own village even now and, though they have been empty since 1937, the old folk still remember the clay-digging, the sandpits up the hill and the regular firing of all manner of clay artefacts. (Today, there is instead a well-known pottery making full use of the valley's clay.)

Here they made everything the village needed. They had begun when a local landlord wanted to drain large areas of the marshy valley and needed land-drain tiles; but they soon realised how good the local clay was and they diversified to make roofing tiles and house bricks for the estate and, gradually, for a much wider area. It happened that not only was the valley's clay ideal (it has the necessary iron content for brick-clay, and indeed there used to be quite an ironworking industry in the area centuries ago) but also the slopes of the hangers provided good sand — and if you are thinking of making your own bricks on your own land, make sure you have both these raw materials close by, and then by trial and error combine them in the right proportions to make bricks that will not collapse or crack in the firing.

Sunbaked bricks (adobe) are not fired but for practical purposes in this country firing is essential in brick-making. The valley clay here was dug in winter, after the topsoil had been set aside and after the chosen site's trees had been cleared for use as fuel in the firing. The dug clay was left to weather until the summer, when a horse brought the clay and sand into the brickyard as required: the animal knew the route from the sandpits so well that he needed no driver. The clay was put into a pit and left to soften under water, then it was transported to the pugmill where the horse, harnessed to a long pole, walked endlessly in circles to mill the clay and make it pliable. Next it was carried to the moulding house where it was rolled on a table and then roughly shaped into blocks, pushed into sanded wooden moulds and levelled off at the top with a wire. The moulds were larger than the eventual bricks as the clay would shrink during the firing. They were then flipped on to pallets, transferred to trolleys and wheeled into the ackhouses to dry naturally for a week or so before being trolleyed to the kiln for firing, twenty thousand at a time.

The kiln was wood-fired: wood-cutting was a winter job and the brickyard foreman would buy a standing coppice crop, felling it to make bundled bavins for the kiln, with a nice little sideline in wooden hoops, pea sticks, bean poles and other coppice produce. Once the kiln fires had been started, they burned continuously for two days and two nights, at fortnightly intervals so that in one week the workforce was filling and firing, and in the second week emptying the kiln and stacking the finished bricks in the yard.

Handmade bricks and roofing or floor tiles are extremely expensive to buy now (and you will soon find out why if you try to produce them yourself) but are in demand for very special building work. An interesting combination could be brick-making and the production of charcoal: both require continuous controlled firing for several days and careful stacking in the kiln. A mud-plastered brick clamp could successfully be fuelled with charcoal.

Tiles

Don't forget to mould frogs for your bricks (on the underboard) and to make nibs and nail-holes for your roofing tiles while the clay is still in the mould. The tiles, hips, valleys and drainpipes can all be fired with the bricks in the same kiln. Curved tiles are first cut flat and then dried over curved moulds. You might have a sideline of plant pots if you have a wheel to throw them on — and remember the drainage holes.

Modern mass-produced decorative tiles are made of clay dust, stamped and pressed into moulds at high speed: a complete fired tile can be produced from dust within forty minutes and you will never be able to equal that rate. But you can press tiles if you wish. The Gambia, where big pottery waterjars are fired on glorious communal bonfires at nightfall, inspired Keith Bennett, a British technical adviser who worked in West Africa for several years, to devise a simple hydraulic press for decorative tiles made from wet clay. He discarded the idea of casting them in moulds using a slip, or hand-pressing clay — both were too tedious for any scale of production — and settled for a hydraulic wet-clay press to produce his patterned tiles at a rate of one a minute. The press Bennett designed cost less than £500 and was made in an agricultural engineering workshop (talk to your blacksmith). It has a six-tonne hydraulic ram and is controlled by various handles and foot-levers. The dies, which have very intricate patterns, are made of high-strength plaster and each can produce about a thousand tiles before needing replacement.

Pottery

The preparation of homeland clay for pottery is similar to that for brick-making, on a smaller scale. Dig it, weather it, break it up and remove stones and other debris, then cover it with water and work it — you can tread it as if you were preparing grapes for wine-making. Sieve out smaller impurities then let it stand for several days so that the clay particles settle and you can siphon off the clear water. Use evaporation or absorption techniques to remove the remaining excess moisture, and then remove all the air from the clay by a combination of bashing, folding and rolling, again and again.

The main steps in producing pottery are:

1 Form it (by throwing, handmaking or in a mould) while the clay is damp and plastic.

2 Dry it naturally to lose free water (it will shrink).

3 Heat it in a kiln to about 1000°C: it will shrink even more and undergo certain chemical changes, becoming hardened.

4 Cool it. At this stage you have *biscuitware* pottery: it is insoluble and permanent but is still porous.

5 Glaze it: cover the object with powdered glass and put it back in the kiln to melt the glaze. Use a glaze appropriate to the temperature of the kiln. If you fire it at 1000–1100°C the glaze will melt but the finish will remain shiny and bright and the pottery will still be somewhat porous: at this stage it is *earthenware*. If it is fired at 1150°C or more, however, the clay itself begins to vitrify, fusing together with the glaze as a solid, denser, heavier mass with a duller glaze which is often mottled: this is *stoneware*, which is usually fired at 1250–1300°C. If you have used special pure clay and a special glaze, fired at stoneware temperatures, you will have *porcelain*, which is light in weight and often translucent.

Forming pottery

The main techniques are pot-coiling, slab-work, moulded pottery and, of course, thrown pots.

To *coil* a pot (a very basic method), roll out a sausage of clay of consistent diameter, without twisting it. Lay it in rings, one on top of another (rather than a continuous spiral), to form the pot walls on a disc-shaped base. Press each roll with your thumb so that its cross-section is slightly oval, and stick everything together with finger pressure, smoothing as you go. The shape of the pot is varied by using different lengths of clay sausage.

Slabwork is used to make square rather than round pots, or boxes or model houses for example. Roll the clay into sheets of uniform thickness, or use an implement like a cheesewire to slice off horizontal sheets from a block. Join the slabs by butting them together and using wet clay or moisture to weld them.

Moulded pottery can be made by putting slabs or very liquid clay (known as casting slip — 'slip' is simply very liquid clay for casting or decorating) into shaped moulds. The slip is made from ball clay, china clay, feldspar and flint with additional materials such as waterglass or sodium carbonate to act as deflocculents. The first step is to make your own moulds with plaster of Paris: use plasticine or solid clay to create a solid form surrounded by a sleeve so that the liquid plaster can be poured between form and sleeve to make the shape you need for the mould.

To *throw* clay on a wheel takes a great deal of skill. At least attend evening classes to learn the basic techniques before you invest in any equipment: some people never do manage to be successfully creative by this method. And certainly do not even think of buying your own kiln until you have had plenty of practical potting experience. Indeed, kiln management is a craft in itself and can make or ruin your work. Kilns demand a lot of space, too, and quite a lot of capital.

Decoration

Pottery of various kinds can be decorated at any stage between formation and glazing — it can be impressed, embossed, pierced, incised, fluted, inlaid, faceted or merely coloured. For *slipware*, apply a decorative layer of slip as if it was a glaze, using very wet clay of a different colour poured over the surface before glazing. Mingle slips of different colours for a marbled effect, or use a feather to create deliberate patterns. There are lots of effective techniques: experiment.

An alternative is to use coloured glazes. For example, you can apply batik techniques by covering parts of the surface with hot wax so that the glaze does not stick to those parts. Metal oxides are used to add colour to clear glazes: iron oxides for colours ranging from straw and ginger to dark brown or black, cobalt for bright blue, copper for peacock green to black or auburn, manganese for purple, nickel for a greyish tone, chromium for dull green, or the yellows of vanadium and antimony. Other colours can be achieved by mixing the pigments.

And then there is potash — the ash from burning wood or other vegetable matter — which is rich in potassium and is used to make glazes of various colours including pale cream, greys, greens and bright oranges, depending on the species which has been burned and the chemistry of the soil in which the plant or tree grew. Put the ash of a woodfire into a bucket of water to let the bits of charcoal and other debris rise to the surface so that they can be skimmed off. The useful ash will sink but be careful: you have created quite a strong alkaline solution — caustic potash — which can dissolve matter left in it. A really concentrated solution can strip paint. The rest of the process involves a lengthy period of waiting and drying the stuff to a black powder before it can be included in a glaze recipe: it has been described in the Woodland Byproducts section.

Once you have learned the basic techniques, you can let your imagination have free rein in decorating the ceramics you have produced. They can be handpainted in a riot of strong colours or delicate pastels, or embellished with three-dimensional designs built up in layers on a plain surface or from moulds. You can, if you prefer, get round all the business and gloriously messy creativity of working the clay: instead, you could work with *greenware* — unfired pieces from a mould — which will enable you to satisfy the urge to decorate rather than fashion. Or you could produce greenware from your own slip-casting and sell it to hobby ceramicists for them to decorate; you could sell tuition, decorating materials and kiln access as a complete package. You can buy readymade moulds of all sorts of

ornaments and containers in order to set up a farm or village ceramics class as a sideline if you have access to a good wholesale supplier.

Possibilities

Pots, platters, bowls, jugs, candlesticks, ornaments, teapots, vases, mirror frames, cups, soup mugs, trays, ashtrays, earrings, pottery animals for your toy farmyard, miniature cottages, calabashes, amphora, urns, flowerpots, plant pots, herb tags, goblets, beakers, jars, casseroles, butter dishes, bread bakers, plate warmers, lamp stands, ceramic bangles and flower brooches, bells, napkin rings, bottles, wall plaques, house nameplates, ceramic tiles, earthenware birdbells and nestboxes, hanging bowls, herb pots, rhubarb forcing-pots, garden planters, chimney pots, wall masks, architectural ceramics from ornate tiles to large terracotta sphinxes and garden fountains, murals, landscapes, portraits, pictures — not to mention the quite different art of modelling in clay. What a versatile medium!

And how about those magically pure white smoking-pipes with stems no thicker than a barley straw? I used to dig them up by the score in my kitchen garden, these cottager's clays which were sold by hawkers all over the country and were bought by the gross or by the barrel. After use, they were put into a piperack and left in the fire or in a brick oven overnight to clean: they came out as good as new the next morning. Here and there some people still make them and endeavour to smoke them. You can buy spanking new 'collector's clay pipes' with ornate bowls in the form of heads, acorns and so on, but the simple, clean style of the original pipe found haphazardly buried in the garden is perhaps more pleasing.

Stone and slate

Slate is compressed shale and, although a strong material, it can be split into layers with a hammer and chisel if you are skilled, or into rectangular blocks. Split slate is an excellent local roofing material and it is also decorative for fireplaces, table tops, the faces of clocks, barometers or thermometers, desk sets, lamps, nesting boxes, bird tables and miniatures.

Stone is ideal for making walls without the 'glue' of mortar, that is, dry stone walling. Every region has its local stone and its own style of walling. Look for the type of stone which can be split to give at least two flat faces. Start by watching an experienced stonewaller at work and by looking closely at local examples of walls. There are books on the subject and you might be able to persuade your local Agricultural Training Board to run a course if enough people are interested, or gain experience by lending your free labour to the British Trust for Conservation Volunteers.

At its most basic, a good wall is two-faced with the cavity between the faces infilled with smaller stones. The foundation stones should be as big as possible and laid absolutely horizontal to give the wall a firm base. The outer faces should be reasonably flat in their vertical plane and built to slope gently inwards from base to top, with the added security of occasional through-stones running across the full width of the wall to bind the two faces together. Lay the building stones more or less in courses, with broken bonding like a brick wall so that the join between two stones in one course is spanned by a stone on the next course. Top the wall with thinner coping stones set vertically on edge across the wall to finish its crown.

Stone masonry and dressing are beyond the scope of this book, whether for building, paving, roof-tiling, tombstones and memorials, carving, sculpting, dressing millstones, or making saddlestones or 'mushrooms' to decorate gardens, either out of 'real' stone or moulded imitations. You could also cast garden planting troughs, urns and statues, or carve figures from limestone, or even make stone jewellery, perhaps decorated with dried flowers under a coat of varnish.

On the subject of sculpture, in passing, you might find inspiration in the work of Andy Goldsworthy's ephemeral art — not so much from its ephemerality as from his imaginative use of materials in the 'sculptures' he creates, photographs and abandons. Some of the materials are themselves ephemeral — snow, ice, growing wildflowers, berries, leaves and grasses coiled into rams-horn spirals and pyramids

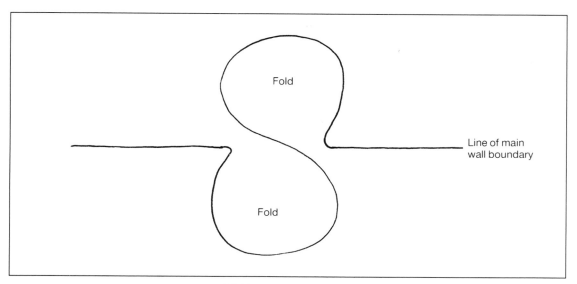

S-FOLD FOR LIVESTOCK

Andy Goldsworthy's stone-wall sculpture, in which the straight run of a field boundary is interrupted by a figure-of-eight, makes two practical livestock folds.

for example — but he also uses pebbles, rocks and stones: my personal favourite is a dry stone wall which incorporates an unexpected figure-of-eight or S-shape built athwart the run of the wall and making an ingenious fold for cattle or sheep — sculpture and practical farming combined!

Metal

As it is most unlikely that you are prepared to dig and refine metal ores from your own land, and as the apprenticeship for metalwork is long and the forge equipment considerable, this is really beyond the scope of the book, however vital the forge once was to the village or however important to the local economy the mining of ore. If you are interested in working iron as a blacksmith or a farrier (the latter, in theory, deals with horses, including shoeing, footcare and a quiet bit of horse veterinary work on the side, along with human tooth-pulling when required), there is ample potential for restoration and decorative ironwork, indoor and outdoor, as well as the more routine repairs to tools and agricultural equipment. Table 11 gives some suggestions.

Steel is more widely used than pure iron now: it is an iron alloy with varying amounts of carbon. Most people use mild steel for blacksmith work, rather than expensive wrought iron, which is pure iron melted and stirred, hammered and squeezed, so that it becomes strong but is fibrous in structure and therefore malleable. Wrought iron lasts a lot longer than mild steel, which is not fibrous but granular; however, mild steel has greater tensile strength and can often be bent without being heated, though it is not advisable in practice.

At Kidwelly, in South Wales, a tinplate works has been restored as an example of the old handmilling process, with steam

TABLE 11

Metalwork

Candlesticks	Plant stands	Nails, doorstuds, coachbolts
Light fittings	Screens and grilles	Barrel hoops
Knives	Bedsteads/heads	Keys
Armoury	Tools	Tethering rings/stakes
Garden furniture	Crooks	House nameplates/numbers
Gates and fences	Air/bat 'bricks'	Pub signs
Mirror frames	Chains	Village signs
Ornaments	Anchors	Window latches
Scrapmetal sculpture	Sheep shears	Signposts
Doorstops	Cowbells, sheepbells	Pumps
Coffee tables	Horse bells/brasses	Cauldrons
Diningroom furniture	School bells	Staircases
Stools	Dinner gongs	Hayracks
Clothes airers	Trivets, meat hooks	Planters
Victorian towel rails	Hinges, gate furniture	Barbecues
Sundials	Door furniture	Street lamps
Fountains	Horsedrawn implements	Pots, pans
Automata	Traps	Cutlery
Toys	Leaded lights	Tongs
Heath Robinson machinery	Bellows	Pergolas
Jugs	Harness and other	Boot scrapers
Weathervanes	buckles	Lead figures
Balconies	Clock faces	Hanging baskets
Urns and vases	Jewellery	Mangers

engines a century old. Tin was of great local importance in some parts of the country and was an essential material for tinkers (the word might come from 'tin' but more likely from the 'tink' sound of their hammers) who fashioned sheet metals, lapped, rivetted or soldered together to form items such as watering cans, pots, jugs, pans and trays. In every century except our own, itinerant tinkers have been a familiar part of life throughout the land. They were, essentially, itinerant: they made and sold their goods and then returned at regular intervals to repair or replace them. I can just about remember the occasional tinker in remote rural areas, and, less then twenty years ago, an itinerant knife-grinder in the heart of London making a remarkably good living by serving the needs of hotel and restaurant chefs. The traditions of the countryside can indeed thrive in the cities.

7 Cottage Offices and Shops

Cottage industries were commonplace in earlier centuries and were indeed essential to the rural economy. Today, however, the cottage office is perhaps a more realistic 'industry' in the countryside and is likely to become even more important as computer-based systems become widely acceptable, affordable and adaptable, while polluting commuting cars become less popular.

The Telecottage Movement

The 'electronic cottage' concept appeals to many who want to combine country living with real income and, if you have a telephone, a microcomputer and a fax machine, you can carry out almost any office job from home (your employer willing), linked invisibly to colleagues scattered across the country and across the world too. You do, of course, need to have plenty of self-discipline and the ability to work happily on your own but you also have a great freedom to keep half an eye on the livestock and to keep in touch with the real world of the countryside, including wildlife and village life if you so wish. It is possible that electronic communications systems will, in fact, 'save the village' by helping people to work where they live, just as they did in every century before the industrial revolution, rather than deserting the place for most of their waking hours. There could even be new life for village shops!

Apart from obvious home-office activities such as acting as a poste restante or telephone point, writing books and articles, typing envelopes (more lucrative than writing!), running a word-processing bureau or working from home for a major company or as a freelance computer programmer or consultant, more satisfying enterprises might include using desktop editing equipment to produce newsletters or more ambitious publications (several authors are already printing their own books), which might eventually lead you into commercial publishing, perhaps combined with video and audio productions.

(A decade ago, when I was a freelance technical author writing manuals for users of agricultural software, I suggested to one company that it should combine the printed word with the programmed monitor image by making nature identification guides. For example, you have seen a pink butterfly with blue polka dots sipping nectar from a daisy in April: what is it? Key in some basic information and your home computer gives you the answer, with a visual screen image as a crosscheck, and refers you to the appropriate page of the accompanying book which gives you colour photographs and all you could ever want to know about the species. A bird guide, I suggested, could also have an audio element to help you identify by song. But they told me that the database would be far too cumbersome. That was then, and the hardware has developed dramatically in the meantime . . .)

If you live in or near a village, there is plenty of scope for setting up a Swedish-style telecottage, preferably in the village hall or school or some other place with reasonable public access. Those who are encouraging the idea describe a telecottage as a room in the village with computers and communications equipment which can be used by local people, either for learning or for work (for the community or for themselves), especially those who, individually, would not otherwise have access to such equipment and could not afford or justify owning it themselves. It could be used for part-time local businesses or for earning pin-money, or for voluntary projects such as publishing a parish magazine. Not only would local people (including children) be encouraged to learn new skills but also the place would act as an important social centre — something which many villages are lacking, especially with the demise of the village shop.

There are plenty of other possibilities if your interest is in the community. How about a reference centre for local history researchers, or a conservation co-ordination centre, or a general help-line for a particular interest, or a consultancy in an unusual field?

Contract work and services

Working from home certainly need not be restricted to paperwork and computers. How about offering your services and skills (supposing that you have them) as a water diviner, a contract milker, an MMB milk recorder, an AI operative, a livestock foot-trimmer, shoer, shearer, lambing assistant or wherever your experience lies, using such contract work as a lifeline while you establish your cottage industry and also to widen your contacts — they are invaluable to any small business.

Or be more ambitious: set up as a minder, looking after pets or livestock on their own premises in the owners' absence and building up a small team of reliable minders to cope with peak periods. If you have the animals and skills, become a specialist contractor with a team of working horses or oxen for farmwork or (more likely) shows, pageants, weddings and similar occasions, and have a small training centre to teach the increasing number of people who have a serious interest in farming with the aid of working animals — skills which were widespread as recently as the 1930s but have now been largely forgotten, though many older farm-workers and woodsmen will have their

memories. More practically, perhaps, invest in an all-terrain vehicle (ATV) and become a contractor for crop-spraying in seasons too wet for heavy tractor wheels in the field. Or think of all those smallholders and small farmers who perhaps lack experience or equipment of some kind: cater for *their* needs. If you have a skill, use it — sell it.

In a wider context, there is a crying need in rural areas for all sorts of small service businesses — providing affordable local transport, delivering groceries, odd-jobbing, window cleaning, springcleaning, plumbing (always in demand), tree surgery, gardening, cooking, listening, teaching crafts in the village hall: there is bound to be a niche for someone with skills, ability, experience, efficiency and affability. But it will be hard work trying to make a living from it unless you are thoroughly professional in your approach, which means complete reliability for a start.

If you are at all serious about turning an interest into a cottage industry of any kind, you *must* have a professional attitude and you must look well ahead.

Cottage shop

The most crucial part of any cottage industry is selling the goods: that is what converts a hobby into a business. However competent your craftsmanship, however brilliant your ideas and designs, however essential your services, no one will buy unless they know what is available, and in a crowded market-place no one will buy unless you can persuade them that *your* goods or services are better or more original than others on offer.

So many cottage industries, using skills and producing items which were once essential to everyday life when there was no competition from mass-production, are now in effect producing luxury goods — the essentials are made far more economically in the factories. You are offering something of yourself in everything you sell and, while that is a vital part of your product, you must look at it from the outside. Okay, it gave you personal satisfaction to make it, whatever it is, and you are really rather proud of yourself, but perhaps the potential purchaser will not appreciate how many hours it took and how much skill it needed, and will think: 'I could make that myself!' and will prefer to do so for the sake of the creative challenge.

There is little point in producing dozens of cute calico cats simply because you like making them: wonder first if anybody else will find them appealing, and work out what sort of person that might be and where they might open their purse, then go for it!

Your soundest move will be to contact the local Rural Development Commission's business service. The RDC (previously known as CoSIRA) has as its main role the promotion of jobs and communities in rural England and has a great deal of experience in such matters which will gladly be shared with you — initially free and subsequently for a modest charge. The business service's objective is to help small businesses to 'start up, grow and prosper in villages and country towns in England'. Local RDC offices can offer or advise on technical training for a range of rural industries at every level from apprentice to master (the Appendix lists courses available at the time of writing, to give an idea of the scope) and there are special advisers on crafts such as farriery, forgework, thatching, saddlery, sawmilling, furniture-making, mechanical engineering, wheelwrighting, ceramics, upholstery, the restoration of antiques and so on. Local business advisers and management consultants will advise on sales and marketing, on buying and running a small shop, a sawmill, a tourist enterprise (including guesthouses, restaurants, activity centres etc.). There are RDC people to advise on buildings and conversions into workshops, or on machinery and equipment, or on budgeting, and sometimes help can be given in a small way with loans as well.

Then there is your regional Agricultural Training Board (ATB) which can sometimes offer very practical training to suit the needs of small groups — perhaps half a dozen people — in certain agricultural and horticultural crafts; the ATB can also organise

training for managers and supervisors to help improve management, business, financial and marketing skills.

The National Federation of Women's Institutes might be able to help in at least two ways. The federation organises and trains people for a Home Economics certificate, for example, which covers a very wide range of skills from wine-making and herb-growing to interior design and more than thirty crafts (see Appendix). Then there are the famous WI markets, known and loved by several generations, where you can sell fresh produce (fruit, vegetables, flowers, eggs, honey), homemade bakes, savouries and preserves or craftwork. All you need to do is to become a WI Market shareholder — five pence to become a member and a small commission deducted on sales but all the rest of the sales cash is paid back to you. There are more than 550 WI markets in England, Wales and the Channel Islands and the experience could be useful before you progress to a regular town market stall or, perhaps, one day, open your own small shop — a farm shop, a barn shop, a cottage shop, a wildfood restaurant, a village shop or an American-style 'green market' for fresh produce.

If you become ambitious enough to set up shop, *please* do your homework first! Too many such schemes fail ignominiously, with the initial enthusiasm dying in a welter of long hours, poor seasons, fluctuating sources of stock or less than supportive families and villagers.

It is never enough just to think how nice it would be to have a shop. The best shops either entice customers with something special, something different, consistently higher standards than average, or (or rather and) combine the shop with other public enterprises so that people who come for one reason find when they arrive that there are other things to do or see or buy and that the family can make an outing of the visit.

The pick-your-own idea, for example, is much more successful if the holding can offer pickers at least fresh fruitjuice or a cup of tea and a homebaked bun in pleasant surroundings with a good view, with consideration for those who are hampered by small children, wheelchairs, creaking joints and so on. PYO with a coffee-and-icecream parlour *and* a shop is an even better idea: initially the shop can sell freshly harvested fruit and vegetables and home-produced bakery, dairy goods and preserves, but as the flow of customers increases it can begin to stock other cottage-industry goods from local smallholders and craftworkers. Here again, like the village telecottage, there is excellent opportunity for encouraging local participation and hence increasing the village's sense of community.

Soon your shop could be selling dyed yarns, hand-knitted garments, pottery, leatherwork, baskets, paintings, herbs, herbal cosmetics, potpourri, honey, country wines, dried flowers, rustic bird tables, wooden toys and carved figurines, spinning wheels, chairs . . . Develop the shop gradually to avoid being overwhelmed with unsaleable stock.

If you are in a tourist area and your shop is well sited and well signposted, perhaps visible from a main road and with plenty of parking space, you will probably find that a minor hobby turns into a major venture, open all weekend and employing several local people. Are you ready for that? Perhaps a mail-order business would be easier to handle? If so, you need to know a lot about marketing. Your catalogue, acting as the shop-window, must be attractively designed and well produced with plenty of good illustrations and descriptive information so that people know exactly what they are buying. Offer original ideas, and, above all, keep your standards consistently high. And good luck to you!

Finally, here are some examples of real cottage industries. In Cornwall, at Cornish Rustics in Tintagel, slate is the local material used for making little models of wells, rustic bridges and buildings 6–12 in high. In Suffolk, at Thurston, the Harts capture English vernacular architecture in hand-painted ceramic cottages, village schools and Georgian houses. Several potteries make simple little terracotta cottages and crofts; some will produce a ceramic model of a customer's own dwelling. But the most exciting miniatures of all must be at Ilton in Somerset, where thirty years ago John Constable began to create his Nursery of Miniatures, a landscape of cottages, gardens and fenced fields made with traditional materials using traditional techniques but all tiny: the fences, for example, are two inches high. The cottages are enchanting with beautifully built walls of real stone and perfectly thatched little rooves, carefully scaled down from real cottages with the right style of wooden windows, and all surrounded with carefully chosen living miniature trees and plants.

Thousands of people live in cottages and thousands more dream of doing so. For the dreamers, the miniatures might be the only reality. Perhaps you could start building and selling tiny local cottages as your cottage industry? City-dwellers, expatriates and Americans would love them!

Appendix I

Dyes

ACACIA (heartwood): lively brown
AGRIMONY (leaves, stalks): butter yellow
ALDER (shoots, in March): yellow to cinnamon (tawny if dried and powdered)
ALDER (bark): tawny red
ALDER (green wood): pinky-fawn
ALDER BUCKTHORN (bark): deep orange
ALKANET (root): slate to pinky-brown
ANNATTO: orange to gold
APPLE (bark): yellow
ASH (bark): green, black, blue
ASH (shavings with bismuth): vigogne
BEARBERRY (leaves): yellow to green-grey
BEARBERRY (dried leaves): violet-grey to charcoal
BIRCH (bark): yellow to tan
BIRCH (inner bark with iron): purple
BIRCH (leaves): yellow
BLACKBERRY (berries): pink, mauve, purple, navy blue
BLACKBERRY (young shoots): grey
BLOODROOT (root): reddish-orange, camel, pink
BRACKEN (young shoots): yellow-green
BRAZILWOOD: pink to grey
BROOM — DYER'S GREENWEED (flowers): yellow to brown
BUCKWHEAT (stalks): blue
CAMOMILE (flowers): bright yellow to olive green
CEDAR (roots): purple
COCHINEAL (insect): pink to purple
COLTSFOOT (plant): greenish yellow
COMFREY (plant): yellow
COREOPSIS (flowers): orange to yellow
COW PARSLEY (leaves): light green
CUTCH: tan to chestnut
DAFFODIL (flowers): sunny yellow

DAHLIA (flowers): orange
DANDELION (roots): magenta
DOCK (root): yellow
DOG'S MERCURY (tops): greyish yellow
ELDER (leaves): greenish yellow, olive, grey-green
ELDER (berries): grey, lovat, lavender, blue, purple
FORSYTHIA (leaves): deep green
FUSTIC (bark chips): yellow to gold
GALL NUTS: dark green
GOLDENROD (flowers, plants): yellow to olive
GRAPE (fruit): blue to purple
GROUND IVY: olive green
HEATHER (flowers, young tips): yellows
HEATHER (fresh branches): green
HENNA: bronze to brown
HOPS (stalks, leaves): yellow
HORSE CHESTNUT (nuts): gold
HORSETAIL, COMMON: yellow to green
ICELANDIC MOSS: orange or brown
INDIGO (leaves): blue
JUNIPER (fresh berries): strong yellow
JUNIPER (dried berries): olive-brown
LADY'S BEDSTRAW (roots): coral
LADY'S BEDSTRAW (tops): yellow
LICHEN CUDBEAR: purple or red
LICHEN ORCHIL: pink to burgundy
LICHENS generally: yellows and reddish-brown
LILY-OF-THE-VALLEY (leaves): green or yellow
LOGWOOD (chips): slate to black
MADDER (root): pink, rich red, brown
MARIGOLD (flowers): cream, pale yellow
MEADOWSWEET (roots): black
MULBERRY (fruit): lavender, blue, purple
NETTLE (plant): grey-green
OAK (bark): browns
ONION (skins): brassy yellow, orange, tan

PARSLEY (fresh): cream
PINE (cones): reddish-yellow
POPLAR (buds): grey to gold and brown
PRIVET (leaves, shoots): strong yellows
PRIVET (berries): greyish green
SAFFLOWER (flowers): yellow, orange, tan, pink
ST JOHN'S WORT (flowers): pinky beige to gold
SANDALWOOD: light red to brown
SANDERSWOOD: copper to tan
SORREL (plant): greyish yellow
SORREL (roots): soft pink
SPINDLE (berries): blue
SUMAC (berries, roots, stem): yellow, orange, tan, grey-black
TANSY (flowers): mustard
TEA (leaves): tan
TURMERIC (root, powdered): golden orange to brown
WALNUT (leaves): creamy fawn to grey
WALNUT (green husks): light to dark brown
WELD/DYER'S ROCKET/ MIGNONETTE: lemon yellow to green

WOAD (leaves): blue
YARROW: yellow
YEW (heartwood): gold to orange-brown
ZINNIA (flowers): yellows

Mordants

Mordants are used to 'fix' elusive dyes, and different mordants can give different shades from the same source material. Old mordants included stag-horn moss or stale urine. Today the following, some of which affect fabric texture as well as colour, are most commonly used:

ALUM (aluminium potassium sulphate) for brightness and clarity
CHROME (potassium dichromate) for depth and permanence
COPPER (copper sulphate) with vinegar for blue-green tint
IRON (ferrous sulphate) to 'sadden' or dull and deepen colour
CREAM OF TARTAR (tartaric acid) often combined with alum
TIN (stannous chloride) to sharpen reds and yellows

Appendix II

Organisations

Rural Development Commission
11 Cowley Street, London SW1P 3NA
141 Castle Street, Salisbury, Wilts SP1 3TP
(formerly CoSIRA)

See local telephone directory for regional offices.

Business Service (formerly known as CoSIRA — Council for Small Industries in Rural Areas) provides information, business management and technical advisory service to small businesses in the countryside; also advice on obtaining finance, premises or training.

Range of advice
FINANCIAL ADVICE on arranging funds; limited loan fund and occasional grants.

BUILDING ADVICE on how to build small factory, convert barn into workshop etc.; building design service, construction advice, specialist design, statutory requirements.

ENGINEERING ADVICE on best type of machinery to buy, planning layouts etc., and vetting of secondhand equipment.

SPECIALIST ADVICE on managing a village shop, rural transport, tourist industry etc.

TRAINING for extra practical skills.

BUSINESS MANAGEMENT:
Accountancy, book-keeping, profit planning, cashflow forecasting, costing, loan/overdraft applications.
Marketing, market research, pricing, distribution, advertising and sales, exports, exhibitions.

Production management, planning/control of production, buying and stock control, staff recruitment, employment legislation, statutory sick pay, supervisor training, microcomputers.

TECHNICAL ADVICE:
Building, structural engineering, joinery, conversions, estimating, thatching (roof construction, materials, fixing methods, ground work, roof work), dry stone walling.

Mechanical engineering, electrical engineering, industrial safety, welding techniques, CNC machine tools, low-cost automation, jig and tool designs, workshop layout, fibreglass lamination, thermoplastics, clay products technology and pottery, abrasive wheels, vehicle electrics, engineering design (agricultural and processing machinery), production engineering, environmental engineering, plastics (injection moulding, extrusion etc.).

Furniture-making, antique furniture restoration, upholstery, woodworking machinery, spraying and finishing, making and restoring horsedrawn vehicles, wheelwrighting, turnery, carving, gilding, veneering, polishing, upholstery.

Sawmill management, timber technology, saw doctoring, round timber, timber conversion.

Farriery (including shoeing and physiology), forgework, general blacksmithing, decorative ironwork, toolmaking, design, metal finishing, power hammers.

Saddlery, leatherwork, bridles, harness.

Engineering projects and prototypes (design and production in RD workshops of jigs, press tools and special-purpose machinery).

CURRENT COURSES:

Buying a village shop; Professional management for small shopkeepers; Sales promotion seminars; Re-use of redundant buildings.

Welding, Fitting, Machinery.

Vehicle electrics.

Glass reinforced plastics (for laminators, engineers, boat-builders etc.).

Craft pottery technology.

Forgework, basic techniques, Art metalwork, Metal sculpture, Copper repoussé work, Farriery.

Saddlery, Harness-making, Leather vessels and bellows, Horse collars.

Thatching.

Furniture restoration including carving, gilding, wood-turning, decorative painting, veneering, colouring, polishing, upholstery, loose covers, industrial sewing machines.

Woodworking machinery.

Seminars for rural builders/joiners (estimates, sales/marketing).

Development Board for Rural Wales

Ladywell House, Newtown, Powys SY16 1JB.

Government agency to promote economic and social development in mid-Wales, especially in manufacturing, agriculture, forestry, fishing, tourism. Advice to small businesses.

Highlands and Islands Development Board

Bridge House, 20 Bridge Street, Inverness IV1 1QR.

Government agency in northern and western Scotland to promote economic and social development. Emphasis on industries common or exclusive to rural areas. Schemes include encouragement of fish and shellfish farms (grants and loans available), special skills training for self-employed or unemployed interested in small business development, crafts assistance to individuals and small businesses in craft industry (discretionary grants for training and consultancy, specialist tuition on technical skills

and processes). The SCOTTISH DEVELOPMENT AGENCY (Rosebery House, Haymarket Terrace, Edinburgh EH12 5EZ) also has a crafts scheme to assist with setting up and equipment costs and training, and a small business finance scheme.

Agricultural Training Board

Summit House, Glebe Way, West Wickham, Kent BR4 0RF.

Training centre: National Agricultural Centre, Stoneleigh.

See local telephone directory for regional offices.

Provides training schemes for people engaged in agricultural or horticultural production and encourages local and co-operative provision of training.

COURSES include:

Skills for horticulture (including enterprise and financial management, and wide range of practical skills and methods).

Garden centres (design/layout/management, customer service and sales, merchandise/planteria display).

Landscaping (crafts, supervision, management).

Almost every rural/agricultural skill, including (for example) sheep-shearing, footcare, spraying, walls, hedging. The local training organiser will discuss training needs with individuals and then arrange most effective training to suit those requirements — craft skills, management and supervision skills. Very practical training, usually about six people per course. Network of national training groups.

National Federation of Women's Institutes

39 Eccleston Street, Victoria, London SW1W 9NT.

Also many local offices.

TRAINING FOR HOME ECONOMICS CERTIFICATE SCHEME:

Cookery (meals); Bakery; Preservation and home freezing; Cake decoration.

Vegetable and herb gardening; Fruit gardening; Decorative gardening; Gardening under glass.

Basketry and allied crafts; Canvaswork; Ceramics; Corndollies and straw-work; Crochet; Dressmaking; Embroidery; Glass engraving; Glove-making; Handknitting; Handspinning; Hand leatherwork; Lace-making; Lampshade making; Machine embroidery; Machine knitting; Metal-work; Patchwork; Quilting; Rug-making; Smocking; Soft furnishing; Soft leather-work; Tailoring; Tatting; Textiles (weaving, spinning, dyeing); Toy-making; Upholstery; Woodcarving.

Interior design; Exhibition work; Flower arranging.

ACTION PACKS FOR GROUPS:

Hanging baskets; Quilting; Pressing flowers and foliage; Artificial flowers; Patchwork; Quilling (papercraft).

ACRE

Stroud Road, Cirencester, Glos. GL7 6JR.

Charity which takes action on jobs, housing, transport, shops and other services in rural areas. The national association of England's 38 Rural Community Councils, working at local and national level to provide information, advice, training and action to improve the quality of life of all those who live and work in the countryside.

Food From Britain

301–344 Market Towers Crescent, Covent Garden Market, London SW8 5NQ.
8–19 Claremont Terrace, Edinburgh.

Administers a range of grants in connection with formation and expansion of agricultural and horticultural co-operatives. Speciality Food Programme to encourage small businesses in speciality food and drink sector.

Ministry of Agriculture, Fisheries and Food

Local offices in telephone directory, also Department of Agriculture and Fisheries for Scotland (DAFS) and Welsh Office Agriculture Department (WOAD).

Farm Diversification Grants scheme to promote alternative farm-based but non-agricultural uses for existing agricultural buildings and land.

Crafts Council

12 Waterloo Place, London SW1 4AU.

Information centre, register of professional craftspeople, slide library, video tapes on various crafts, information on courses/suppliers of materials/craft fairs and markets/exhibitions. Fact sheets on wide range of crafts with details of societies and guilds, courses, journals, suppliers etc. Craft magazines (and back-numbers in archives). Own bimonthly magazine *Crafts*. Everything a craftworker needs to know . . .

General fact sheets include: Setting up in business; Setting up as a craftsperson; Grants and loans for craft businesses; Marketing; Craft fairs; and many more.

Useful Addresses

For addresses of craft guilds and societies, consult the Craft Council.

ACRE — see Appendix II.

AGRICULTURAL TRAINING BOARD — see Appendix II.

FRED ALDOUS LTD
The Handicraft Centre, PO Box 135, 37 Lever Street, Manchester M60 1UX.
  Mail-order suppliers of homecraft materials and leaflets.

CRAFTS COUNCIL — see Appendix II.

DRY STONE WALLING ASSOCIATION OF GREAT BRITAIN
YFC Centre, NAC, Kenilworth, Warwickshire CV8 2LG.

DRYAD
PO Box 38, Northgates, Leicester.
  Mail-order suppliers, also wide range of craft guides.

FIBRECRAFTS
Style Cottage, Lower Eashing, Godalming, Surrey GU7 2QD.
  Suppliers of spinning/weaving/dyeing equipment and materials. Substantial range of books on fibrecrafts.

FOOD FROM BRITAIN — see Appendix II.

HOOKE COLLEGE
Beaminster, Dorset.
  John Makepeace's school for woodcrafts.

THE LACE HALL
High Pavement, Nottingham NG1 1HF.
  Permanent exhibition of traditional lace.

MUSEUM OF ENGLISH RURAL LIFE
University of Reading, Whiteknights, Reading RG6 2AG.
  Permanent exhibition and archives — agricultural tools and implements, rural industries, domestic equipment.

NATIONAL FEDERATION OF WOMEN'S INSTITUTES — see Appendix II.

NORTHERN IRELAND LOCAL ENTERPRISE DEVELOPMENT UNIT
LEDU House, Upper Gallwally, Belfast BT8 4TB.

RURAL DEVELOPMENT COMMISSION — see Appendix II.

TELECOTTAGES UK
Norsebury Cottage, 91 Winchester Road, Micheldever, Hants SO21 3DG.

TEN HENS
The Gables, Framingham Pigot, Norwich NR14 7QJ.

THATCHING ADVISORY SERVICE
Rose Tree Farm, 29 Nine Mile Ridge, Finchampstead, Berks RG11 4QD.
  Courses run by Bob West.

WALES CRAFTS COUNCIL
20 Severn Street, Welshpool, Powys SY21 7AD.

WEST DEAN COLLEGE
West Dean, Chichester, West Sussex PO18 0QZ.
  Wide range of crafts courses, short or long.

WOOD-MIZER
c/o Marlwood Ltd., 5 Marlpit Close, Edenbridge, Kent TN8 6BE.

Bibliography

A.A./CoSIRA: *Craft Workshops in the English Countryside* (1986).

AARON, J. R.: *The Production of Wood Charcoal in Great Britain* (Forestry Commission).

ALLABY, Michael: *The Survival Handbook* (Pan, 1977).

ARNOLD, James: *Farm Waggons and Carts* (David & Charles, 1977).

ARNOLD, James: *The Shell Book of Country Crafts* (1968).

BARBER, Joel: *Wild Fowl Decoys* (Dover Publications Inc., Mineola, NY).

BAXTER, J.: *The Library of Agricultural and Horticultural Knowledge* (J. Baxter, Lewes, 3rd edition, 1834).

BLACK, M.: *Home-made Butter, Cheese and Yogurt* (EP Publishing, Wakefield, 1977).

BREMNESS, Lesley: *The Complete Book of Herbs* (Guild Publishing 1988/Dorling Kindersley and National Trust).

BRIDGEWATER, Alan and Gill: *The Craft of Wood Carving* (David & Charles, 1981).

BRILL, Edith: *Cotswold Crafts* (Batsford).

BROAN, David and Freda: *Cane and Rush Seating* (Bishopsgate Press, 1987).

BURGESS, Linda, and RICHARDSON, Rosamond: *Country Harvest* (1990).

CAMPBELL, Scott D.: *The Complete Book of Birdhouse Construction for Woodworkers/Easy-to-make Bird Feeders for Woodworkers* (Dove Publications Inc., Mineola, NY).

CENTRE for Alternative Technology: *Tools and Devices for Coppice Crafts* (reprinted by CAT from NFYFC 1957 original).

COBBETT, William: *Cottage Economy* (1823, reprinted Landsman's Bookshop, 1974).

COOPER, Michael: *Discovering Farmhouse Cheese* (Shire, 1978).

CRAFTS Council: *Running a Workshop — Basic Business for Craftspeople* (revised 1989).

CROWTHER, R. E., and EVANS, J.: *Coppice* (Forestry Commission, 2nd edition, 1986).

CURTIS, Susan, FRASER, Romy, and KOHLER, Irene: *Neal's Yard Natural Remedies* (Arkana/Penguin, 1988).

DAVID, Elizabeth: *Spices, Salts and Aromatics in the English Kitchen* (Penguin, 1970).

DAY, Ivan: *Perfumery with Herbs* (Darton, Longman & Todd with the Herb Society, 1979).

DUFF, Gail: *A Book of Pot-Pourri* (Orbis, 1985).

EDLIN, H. L.: *Woodland Crafts in Britain* (Batsford, 1949).

ELEY, G.: *Wild Fruit and Nuts*.

FILBEE, Marjorie: *Cottage Industries* (David & Charles, 1982).

FOOD from Britain: *Food Focus* (2 volumes).

FOSSELL, Theo: *Walking and Working Sticks* (Apostle Press).

GARNER, Lawrence: *Dry Stone Walls* (Shire, 1984).

GRANTZ, Gerald J.: *Home Book of Taxidermy and Tanning* (Stockpole Books, Pittsburgh, Pa., 1969).

GRAVENEY, Charles: *Woodcarving for Beginners* (Studio Vista, 1967).

HARTLEY, Dorothy: *The Land of England* (Macdonald, 1979).

HEPPER, Camilla: *Herbal Cosmetics* (Thorsons, 1987).

HILL, Jack: *The Complete Practical Book of Country Crafts* (David & Charles, 1979).

H.M.S.O.: *Culinary and Medicinal Herbs* (4th edition, 1980).

HOLTOM, Josie A., and HYLTON, William H. (ed): *The Complete Guide to Herbs* (Rodale Press, Aylesbury, 1979).

INTERNATIONAL Labour Office (Geneva): wide range of titles for small-scale industries.

JOBSON, Allan: *Household and Country Crafts* (Elek Books, 1953).

JOHNSTONE, W. Derrick, et al: *Country-work* (ACRE, 1990).

KINSMAN, Francis: *The Telecommuters* (John Wiley & Sons, 1987).

MILK Marketing Board: *On-Farm Cheese Makers of England and Wales*.

PORTER, Valerie: *Enterprises for Small-holders* (and other titles).

PRACHT, Klaus: *Woodturning* (Dover Publications Inc., Mineola, NY).

RASE and others: *British Country Foods Directory*.

ROME, John: *The Blandford Book of Traditional Handicrafts* (Blandford, 1981).

SEAGER, Elizabeth (ed): *The Countryman Book of Village Trades and Crafts* (David & Charles, 1978).

SEYMOUR, John: *The Forgotten Arts* (Dorling Kindersley, 1984).

SHEEN, Joanna: *Pressed Flowers, Creating and Styling* (Merehurst).

SIMMONS: *Turning Wool into a Cottage Industry*.

SPARKES, Ivan G.: Woodland Craftsmen (Shire, 1977).

STOWE, E. J.: *Thatching of Rick and Barn* (Landsman's Library, 1954).

STREET, Len, and SINGER, Andrew: *The Backyard Dairy Book* (Prism Press, Dorchester, 1975).

THEAR, Katie: *The Home Dairying Book* (Broad Leys Publishing Co., Saffron Walden, 1978).

TITTERINGTON, Rosemary: *Growing Herbs* (Crowood, 1987).

TUFTON, Otis: *American Indian Basketry* (Dover Publications Inc., Mineola, NY).

UNITED States Department of Agriculture: *Vacation Homes and Cabins*.

VAUGHAN, M., and HARDIMAN-JONES, M.: *Fruity Passions* (BBC, 1990).

VEREY, Rosemary: *The Scented Garden* (Mermaid, 1981).

WALPOLE, Lois: *Creative Basket Making* (Collins).

WEISS, Ruth: *Set Up and Run a Successful Farm Shop* (Broad Leys Publishing).

WEST, Robert C.: *Thatch — a manual for owners, surveyors, architects and builders* (David & Charles, 1987).

Also a wide range of publications by SHIRE, DRYAD, DOVER, SEARCH PRESS, LEISURECRAFT and others.